Guide to Herbs

A comprehensive guide to herbs

GW00391183

Jenny Linford

Bath · New York · Singapore · Hong Kong · Cologne · Delhi
Melbourne · Amsterdam · Johannesburg · Auckland · Shenzhen

First published by Parragon in 2012

Parragon
Queen Street House
4 Queen Street
Bath BA1 1HE, UK
www.parragon.com

See page 144 for photograph copyright details
Text © Parragon Books Ltd 2012

Produced by Guy Croton

ISBN 978-1-4454-6990-4

Printed in China

Contents

Directory of herbs 22

6

Appendix: Table of usage 134

What is a **herb?**

Throughout history mankind has benefited from plants in many different ways: fundamentally for food and shelter, yet also for several other purposes, including medicine, perfume, and cosmetics. Among these valuable plants is one group with a long history of use which we know as herbs.

When one asks the question what is a herb, one begins to realize how wide any definition must be. Botanists use the term to refer to a plant with a stem that is not woody, yet the word has taken on a larger meaning. A keen cook would probably first think of a herb being a plant employed to add flavor in cooking, such as bay leaves, basil, or thyme. On the other hand, some people might consider herbs to be plants that are drawn on medicinally, such as echinacea or aloe vera. Mankind, however, has used herbs in many other diverse and ingenious ways: as insect repellents, for strewing on floors, and scenting linen; for cosmetics and perfumery, for washing, preserving, and in embalming. This book, therefore, defines herbs as being plants with a history of use, whether that be as a flavoring or food (though the major food plants are not covered in this book), an aid to health, for perfume and cosmetics,

right Purple
loosestrife is
native to Europe,
Asia, and North
Africa and has
long been used
medicinally.

or yet other purposes. Herbs are often plants that are seen as health-giving or beneficial.

Herbs range in size from low-growing plants, such as thyme or oregano, through shrubs such as witch hazel, wormwood, or box, and creepers such as honeysuckle, to trees such as the bay or the curry tree. Mankind's extensive history of utilizing herbs provides examples of every part of the plant being valuable. Leaves are

probably the part of the herb most often used: for flavoring in cooking, eating as a vegetable, making herbal infusions, and for other purposes. Stems, which transport nutrients for the plant, are also used, with lemon grass being an example of a plant stem with a culinary purpose. Flowers, often valued particularly for their fragrance, contain the most active ingredients when they first open fully and are best harvested in dry weather. There are many herb flowers used for a number of different purposes, such as teas, cordials, and cosmetics, among them elderflower, chamomile, and lavender. Herb seeds are employed in many ways, including flavor (caraway, poppy, or fenugreek), to treat stomach pains (fennel seeds) and oil (safflower). Herb berries include juniper, which famously gives gin its distinctive taste, and elderberries, used to make country wines. Herb roots (the underground part of the plant which absorbs water and nutrients), rhizomes (the underground stem from which roots grow), and bulbs (underground storage organs) are all widely used in different ways. Garlic bulbs, for example, are eaten around the world, valued for their healthy properties as well as their flavor. Horseradish roots, with their fiery, pungent flavor, are used as a popular condiment in certain European countries.

Throughout history, all around the globe different cultures have made use of the plants that grew wild around them, with herbs being a wonderful natural resource. A traditional knowledge of the uses and the dangers of the plants that could be found in hedgerows, forests, and fields was helpful, and sometimes invaluable, particularly in the case of medicinal herbs.

above *Popular culinary herbs, such as basil, thyme, and mint, are grown commercially to supply the needs of supermarkets.*
left *Lavender has long been valued for both its therapeutic properties and for its powerful fragrance.*

Herb **gardens**

There is a long history of cultivating herbs in gardens of their own, dating back to Ancient Egypt, where herbs were used extensively in temples for rituals and cleansing. In Islamic cultures, useful plants were grown within enclosures. Roman villa grounds also traditionally included extensive herb gardens.

In Europe, monasteries played an important part for centuries in maintaining the knowledge of cultivating herbs. St. Benedict, who founded the hugely influential Benedictine monastic order in Monte Cassino, Italy, *c.* AD 530, wrote his Rules, a set of precepts for monastic life that have been closely followed since. He ordered that "all the necessaries" for the monks should be available within the monastery walls, emphasizing the importance of the monastery garden.

The sixteenth century saw the rise of the Physic Garden, that is, a garden devoted to plants related to medicine or "physic." Medieval universities created herb gardens for educational purposes: Italy saw the establishment of Europe's first Botanic Gardens, at Pisa in 1543, Padua in 1545 and at Florence in 1550, each of them designed as medical teaching collections. In 1621 Oxford's Physic Garden was founded, now known as the Oxford Botanic Garden. In 1673 the Chelsea Physic Garden was created in London by the Worshipful Society of Apothecaries in order to teach its apprentices to identify and use plants. The

right and opposite Herb gardens are traditionally well ordered, with geometric beds divided by paths and hedges.

Royal Botanic Gardens at Kew, London, traces its ancestry to a Physic Garden, established by Princess Augusta in 1759.

The sixteenth century in England also saw the rise of the knot garden, composed of flower beds laid out in intricate, geometric patterns, with each bed defined by low-cut, evergreen hedges. Although not herb gardens as such, these knot gardens often contained many of the fragrant plants that we think of as herbs. The passion for formal gardens continued in the seventeenth and eighteenth centuries in Europe with the fashion for landscape gardening among the aristocracy. Great houses, such as the stately French chateaux, had their formal herb gardens elegantly laid out in hedge-trimmed beds, performing both an aesthetic and a practical function. On a more humble level, cottage gardens also grew herbs for cookery and for healing purposes. The herb lawn, grown from fragrant, low-growing herbs, such as chamomile or varieties of thyme, has long been a popular

feature of herb gardens. Today, people continue to grow herbs in a variety of ways, from windowboxes containing easy-to-grow staples, such as parsley, mint, or chives, to more classically structured herb gardens.

above *Box hedges are traditionally used to define the borders of herb gardens.*

Herbal **knowledge**

Knowledge of herbs, their properties, and their perils has been passed down both orally and in written form for centuries, sometimes for millennia. With herbs having been used by man since the earliest times, many of them feature in myths and legends and have associations with folklore.

Among the cultures with a venerable history of using herbs medicinally for thousands of years are the Ancient Chinese and the Indians with Ayurvedic medicine.

In classical times a number of important texts were written, including two botanical treatises written by the Greek philosopher Theophrastus around 300 BC; *Historia Plantarum (Enquiry into Plants)* and *De Causis Plantarum (Growth of Plants)*. In

right *Basil is traditionally associated with love.*

AD 77 Pliny the Elder, a Roman natural historian, wrote *Historia Naturalis (Natural History)*, which included the medical uses of herbs. In AD 100 a Greek physician named Dioscorides wrote *De Materia Medica*, listing 950 curative substances of which 600 are from plants. Each entry contained a drawing and description of the plant, an outline of its medicinal qualities and method of preparation as well as warnings about any undesirable effects. This hugely influential herbal remained a standard reference book in western society until around AD 1600. About fifty years after Dioscorides' landmark work, the Greek physician Galen produced *De Simplicibus*, another hugely influential medical book, laying out the theory of the "humors."

Until the fifteenth century European herbals were manuscripts handwritten in Latin, which only a few people could read. With the invention of printing in 1440, there was a rise in the number of herbals. In 1517 a Swiss alchemist known as Paracelsus published a herbal explaining the Doctrine of Signatures, which said that healing herbs had signs in their appearance given by God to indicate their use. After European explorers and colonizers discovered the "New World" of the Americas, a Spanish physician and botanist, Nicolás Monardes, produced the first American herbal in 1574, translated into English as *Joyfull Newes Out of the Newe Founde Worlde*. In the late sixteenth century the herbalist and gardener John Gerard wrote one of the first herbals to be written entirely in English, *The Herball, or Generall Historie of Plants*, still referred to. In 1652 the astrologer and herbalist Nicholas Culpeper produced *The English Physician, or an Astrologo-Physical Discourse of the Vulgar Herbs of this Nation*. This book, in which Culpeper drew upon the Doctrine of Signatures and his knowledge of astrology as well as herbs, was to become one of the bestselling herbals of all time.

Herbs in folklore, myths, and legend

With so many herbs used by man since the earliest times, it is not surprising that a number of them feature in myths and legends and have much folklore associated with them. Yarrow stalks were used in foretelling by the druids and in Ancient China, and the herb's Latin name, *Achillea millefolium*, refers to its associations with the Greek mythic hero Achilles, who is said to have used yarrow to staunch his warriors' wounds during the Trojan War. Myrtle was held to be sacred to the goddess Aphrodite and used in weddings. Betony, used by the Anglo-Saxons against elf sickness, was traditionally planted in churchyards and cemeteries to offer protection against witchcraft. Other herbs with magical associations include mugwort, linked to witchcraft and fertility rituals; witch hazel, traditionally used for divining; and great mullein, thought to drive away evil spirits.

above An illustration of calendula based on those from De Materia Medica *by Pedanius Dioscorides.*

13

Culinary herbs

Herbs have long been used to add flavor to food, drinks, and confectionery. Some herbs are used around the world, while others are associated with distinct cuisines. Garlic, with its powerful odor and taste, is used almost universally. In Southeast Asia, lemon grass, with its citrus flavor, is a key ingredient.

In European cookery, certain herbs are widely used in a number of countries while others are particularly redolent of specific cuisines. Basil, for example, with its strong, sweet scent, evokes Italian cuisine, and is famously a key ingredient of pesto, the Genoese sauce made from fresh basil, pine nuts, garlic, olive oil, and grated Parmesan cheese, traditionally served with *trenette* pasta. Associated with Scandinavia, dill is often used in fish dishes, such as Sweden's famous gravadlax (salmon marinated with rock salt, dill, lemon, sugar, and pepper). Aromatic bay leaves are one of the most widely used herbs in European and North American kitchens, added to stews, sauces, and marinades. Rosemary crops up across Europe, combined with lamb in many countries, as its sharp aroma cuts across the meat's fattiness. In classical French cookery, certain combinations of herbs are traditional, such as *fines herbes* (chopped parsley, chervil, tarragon, and chives), *herbes de Provence* (thyme,

right *Garlic is an important herb in both eastern and western cultures.* far right *Parsley, one of the classic French "fines herbes."*

rosemary, bay, basil, and savory) and *bouquet garni*, a herb bundle usually consisting of parsley, thyme, and bay leaves. In Britain, popular culinary herbs include curly parsley, chives, and mint, with the latter added to new potatoes and peas or made into mint sauce. Strong-flavored sage is classically used in stuffings or to season sausages and cheese.

In China, garlic is the herb most widely used, adding flavor to dishes from stir-fries to slow-braised hotpots. Fresh coriander crops up as a garnish and in dishes such as beef or fish soup. Chinese chives, with their robust, garlic-like flavor, are treated as a vegetable rather than a herb.

Indian cuisine is famous for its use of spices, but alongside these a number of herbs are widely used. Fresh coriander, for example, is blended with green chillies and lemon juice to make a zingy, piquant fresh chutney. Fresh mint is also used in North Indian cookery to make chutneys, flavor appetizers, and, traditionally, rice pilaf dishes. A herb that is particularly characteristic of South Indian cuisine is the curry leaf, from the curry tree. It is added as an aromatic but not eaten.

In the Middle East, flat-leafed parsley is a key flavoring in its own right rather than a garnish, taking center stage particularly in dishes such as Lebanese tabbouleh.

In Southeast Asian kitchens, lemon grass, with its citrus flavor, is a key ingredient. Glossy green kaffir lime leaves are often added whole to recipes. Fresh, strong-flavored, coriander features in Thai cooking, and the Thais also use the plant's roots, crushed with garlic and pepper, to flavor meat and fish.

above left *Many people consider herbal teas to be a soothing alternative to traditional Indian tea.*

above right *Rosehips are high in vitamin C and can be used to make herbal teas as well as jams and jellies.*

15

Herbs in **medicine**

For centuries, all around the world, herbs have been used for healing and treatment. With many herbs growing widely in the wild, these plants were an invaluable form of free medicine, available to those who knew how to use them. Medicinal herbs were also deliberately cultivated for use by specialist practitioners.

Indian Ayurvedic medicine views health as being a harmony between body, mind, and spirit. This system of medicine uses herbs extensively.

China, too, has a venerable history of using herbs medicinally. Herbs in this form of medicine are classified according to the six tastes as pungent, sweet, sour, bitter, salty, or bland, with each taste having a particular use in treatment. A seminal textbook was Li Shizhen's *Compendium*

right The castor oil plant was used as a purgative but the seeds are highly toxic if eaten.

of Materia Medica, a 53-volume work compiled in 1578 during the Ming dynasty and still referred to today.

In the west, much herbal knowledge was passed down from the Ancient Greeks and Romans. The Arabs also added considerably to herbal knowledge, with one essential Arab contribution being the separation of essential oils from herbs by the process of distillation. During the Middle Ages, the healing powers of herbs was an area of knowledge nurtured for centuries by the Christian monasteries. The Middle Ages then saw the rise of the apothecaries, who became specialists in making up herbal medications.

Twentieth-century France saw the development of aromatherapy, the use of essential oils for health. Scented oils were used by many historic cultures, such as the Ancient Egyptians, but the term was coined in 1928 by a French

chemist and perfumier named René-Maurice Gattefossé, who discovered the healing powers of lavender oil by chance when he burned his own hand. Today, aromatherapy and Bach Flower Remedies, the use of flower essences developed in the 1930s by Dr Edward Bach, both enjoy a popular following.

In North America, the Native American tribes had an extensive knowledge of the healing properties of the plants around them and some European settlers drew upon this source of information. An important movement in North America's use of herbs was founded by one Samuel Thomson, whose dangerously ill wife was cured through traditional herbal remedies. This cure inspired Thomson to develop a series of treatments, drawing on Native American herbal treatments, known as the "Thomsonian System" of medicine and in 1822 he wrote his popular *New Guide to Health, or Botanic Family Physician*. The 1830s in North America saw the foundation

of the Eclectic Medical Institute, a term coined by a doctor living among Native Americans, which promoted the use of medicinal herbs.

Throughout human history, herbs have been prepared in various different ways for medicinal purposes. Herbal infusions, taken internally, are made by steeping fresh or dried herbs in hot water, an easy and accessible way to use these plants, especially their leaves and flowers. Decoctions, made from roots, bark, and berries, involve actively boiling the herb. Tinctures are made by steeping herbs in alcohol, a process that preserves the herb in a potent and portable form. Sweetened herbal syrups are a way of making bitter or unpleasant-tasting herbs more palatable. Ointments, made from herbs dissolved in an oil or fat, are applied externally and form a protective layer on the skin.

above left
Scented candles as well as essential oils are used in aromatherapy.
left *Despite its delicate appearance, the opium poppy is the source of a powerful drug.*

Cosmetic **herbs**

Herbs have been used in beauty products for centuries for a variety of purposes: adding fragrance, cleansing the body, and treating blemishes. Many herbs are still incorporated into commercial make-up products to this day and there has been a massive revival in the popularity of natural herb-based cosmetics.

Perfumed oils scented with herbs were used in Ancient Egypt, India, and Persia and the use of perfumes in a variety of forms continued to be popular in classical Greece and Rome, where bath-houses played an important part in society. The Arab discovery in the Middle Ages of how to distil essential herbal oils was an important breakthrough in their use in fragrances.

Certain herbs were valued for their astringent properties, such as yarrow, used to treat greasy hair or oily skin. Rosemary was traditionally added to a tonic rinse to add luster to dull hair and against dandruff. It was also used in Queen of Hungary water, an early toilet water dating back to the fourteenth century. On the other hand, marsh mallow, with its mucilaginous roots, was valued

right Rosemary is a great ingredient to use in anti-aging creams, as it has excellent toning and binding effects.
far right The leaf of wild strawberry is made into a decoction, which is used as an astringent for oily complexions.

for its soothing properties, used for dry skin or chapped hands. The roots and leaves of the wild strawberry were also seen as cooling, recommended by the seventeenth-century herbalist Nicholas Culpeper "to take away any redness in the face, or spots, or other deformities in the skin, and to make it clear and smooth."

Baths have historically been perfumed by the addition of herbal infusions or decoctions. Aromatic, strong-smelling lavender, with its generic name deriving from the Latin verb "to wash" and its antiseptic properties, has a long and particular association with cleansing, traditionally used in soothing baths to relax muscles and also in perfumery.

The cosmetic uses of herbs are varied and ingenious: horsetail, high in silica, is a traditional treatment for brittle fingernails. Chamomile is used in a rinse to lighten fair hair, elder to reduce freckles, and marigold petal infusions to treat eczema and acne. The mint family, long used to freshen breath, is today widely used in toothpastes. One particularly curious practice during medieval times was the use of the juice of deadly nightshade to dilate the pupils of women's eyes, making them appear large and lustrous.

above left *German chamomile.*
above right *Calendula oil is extracted from marigold petals to make skin creams.*
left *Heartsease was used in the treatment of eczema.*

Preserving **herbs**

One of the characteristics that makes herbs so versatile and gives them so many different practical applications is the fact that they are very easy to preserve. This is most commonly done by using one of three methods—drying, freezing, and immersion in oil or vinegar. Preserved herbs can then be used in cooking, fragrant potpourri, or a wide variety of flower arrangements.

Drying

Drying has long been a way of preserving herbs. Many culinary herbs, such as bay or oregano, keep their flavor well when dried or even have it enhanced by the drying process, so are traditionally used in dried form as well as fresh. The purpose of drying is to preserve the essential oils while driving out the plant's water content.

Freezing

Fresh culinary herbs can also usefully be frozen, a process that works well with soft-leafed herbs, such as mint or parsley, retaining their flavor, color, and vitamins. Herbs that have been frozen can be used directly in cooking, with no thawing necessary. It is very easy to freeze most herbs: simply bag them up in your freezer.

right Oregano is easily dried and stored for culinary purposes.
far right The best way to preserve spearmint is to freeze it and then use it unthawed in cooking.

Herbed oils and vinegars

Another popular, traditional way of preserving the flavor of herbs is to add them to oils or vinegars, which are then used in turn for salad dressings, sauces, or marinades. The other advantage of this technique is that bottles and decanters of preserved herbs often look very attractive and so are widely used for decorative as well as culinary purposes.

Potpourri

Potpourri is a fragrant mixture of dried flowers and herbs. The term derives from the French for "rotten pot," being originally a moist mixture of pickled flowers and leaves. Rose petals and lavender flowers are staple ingredients while fragrant herbs, such as mints, sage, lemon verbena, and rosemary, are also popular. Certain herb flowers, including calendula and tansy, keep their color well when dried, adding visual appeal. Ground aromatic orris is a traditional fixative in potpourris. Herbal essential oils are a simple way of adding fragrance to the mixture. Potpourri displayed in a pretty bowl both looks attractive and scents the air around it.

above *Olive oil is a traditional preservative for many different kinds of herb.*
left *Dried herbs are a major ingredient of scented potpourri.*

directory
of **herbs**

The main part of this book comprises a selection of the very best aromatic, culinary, medicinal, and ornamental herbs from around the world. Over 100 magnificent herbs are arranged in alphabetical order by their Latin names, with detailed information about their origins, uses, and individual horticultural preferences, as well as fascinating anecdotes about how their common names came about and much more.

English Mace

Achillea ageratum

Native to Switzerland, English mace is cultivated in Northern Europe, though it is something of a rarity. Its generic name *Achillea* refers to Achilles, the hero of Greek mythology, who is reputed to have been taught the medicinal uses of herbs by the centaur Chiron. Medicinally, it was traditionally taken internally to treat stomach disorders. As a culinary herb, its mildly aromatic leaves can be used to flavor stuffing for roast chicken, added to soups, or sprinkled over pasta, rice, or potato dishes. Its pretty flowers can be dried and incorporated into dried flower arrangements; it is also an ornamental herb to grow in the garden.

Other names: Garden mace, maudlin, sweet milfoil, sweet Nancy

Plant family: Asteraceae

Height: 12–18in (30–45cm)

Habit: Hardy perennial with narrow, deeply serrated, bright green leaves, and clusters of small, cream flowers

Habitat: Well-drained soil in sun

Uses: Culinary, medicinal, decorative

Yarrow

Achillea millefolium

Found growing wild in wasteland and meadows in Asia, Europe, and North America, yarrow has a venerable history as a medicinal herb. Its Latin name refers to the mythical Greek warrior Achilles, who applied yarrow to staunch the wounds of his warriors during the Trojan War. Other traditional medicinal uses for yarrow were to reduce heavy menstruation and against cold and flu. Yarrow infusions are also added to shampoos to treat greasy hair. As well as its many reputed medicinal properties, yarrow is a plant with magical associations; yarrow stalks were used by the Ancient Chinese for foretelling and the druids for divining. Although its culinary applications are limited, young yarrow leaves can be added to salads.

Other names: Carpenter's weed, millefoil, nose-bleed, soldier's woundwort

Plant family: Compositae

Height: Up to 3ft (90cm)

Habit: Hardy perennial with green, feathery, fernlike leaves and flat heads of tiny, pink-tinged, white flowers

Habitat: Waysides and fields in a sunny position

Uses: Culinary, medicinal, cosmetic

Monkshood

Aconitum napellus

Despite its attractive appearance, monkshood has long been known as a highly poisonous plant, with all parts of the plant from the roots to the leaves being dangerous. In Greek mythology, it was rumored to have sprung from the spittle dropped from the jaws of Cerberus, the monstrous three-headed dog that guarded the gates of Hades. It has long been mentioned in herbals both as a source of poison and also as an antidote against other poisons, particularly snake venom. Gardeners growing monkshood should wear gloves when handling it. The name "monkshood" is a reference to the hooded, deep-blue, delphinium-like flowers, which allow the plant to be pollinated only by bees.

Other names: Wolf's bane, friar's cap
Plant family: Ranunculaceae
Height: 4–5ft (1.2–1.5m)
Habit: Hardy perennial with deeply lobed, green leaves and tall spires of deep blue flowers
Habitat: Moist soil in the shade, such as in stream banks or ditches
Uses: Medicinal

Anise Hyssop

Agastache foeniculum

Native to North America, this herb was introduced into Europe only in the nineteenth century. As its common name suggests, it has a distinctive aniseed scent and flavor. Its fragrant leaves are added to salads and also used to make a herbal infusion or added to summer fruit cups. Its summer spikes of flowers are a good source of nectar, notably attractive to butterflies and bees. It is, therefore, a popular plant with beekeepers, producing a fine, anise-flavored honey. Growing in neat clumps, it is popular as an ornamental addition to herb gardens. Medicinally, it was used by Native Americans to treat coughs.

Other names: Anise mint, giant hyssop, fennel hyssop
Plant family: Labiatae
Height: Up to 2ft (60cm)
Habit: Hardy perennial with pointed, ovate, mid-green, toothed leaves and spikes of small, light purple flowers
Habitat: Freedraining, rich soil
Uses: Culinary, decorative, medicinal

Agrimony

Agrimonia eupatoria

Found growing wild throughout Europe in fields, hedgerows, and waste ground, agrimony has long been valued for its medicinal properties. Its name is thought to come from the Greek *agremone,* which means "plant that can heal diseases of the eye," while *eupatoria* in its Latin name is a reference to the first-century BC King Mithridates VI Eupator, renowned for his knowledge of herbal medicines. Over the centuries, notable herbalists have recommended agrimony as a purgative and a treatment for liver complaints, and for curing sores, wounds, and coughs. It has a high tannin content and consequently has an astringent action. Agrimony's dried leaves and flowers are used as the base for mouth gargles, tonics and dressings.

Other names: Cockleburr, sticklewort
Plant family: Rosaceae
Height: Up to 3ft (90cm)
Habit: Hardy perennial with downy leaves, divided into leaflets and long spikes of small, yellow flowers
Habitat: Well-drained soil in sunshine
Uses: Medicinal, culinary

Bugle

Ajuga reptans

Native to Europe, North Africa, and West Asia, this fast-growing perennial thrives in damp woods and grassy fields. The famous seventeenth-century herbalist Culpeper valued it highly in treating wounds and also as a cure for hangovers. Its astringent properties have made it a traditional homeopathic treatment for throat irritations and mouth ulcers, with its leaves used both fresh and dried. Gardeners value the fact that it provides good ground cover, often growing it at border edges or underneath shrubs, and it is also popular with bees and butterflies. A bronze-leafed form, known as bronze bugle, is particularly popular as an ornamental garden plant.

Plant family: Lamiaceae
Height: 4–12in (10–30cm)
Habit: Evergreen perennial, with oval to spoon-shaped leaves and whorled spikes of purplish-blue flowers
Habitat: Moist soil in sun or partial shade
Uses: Medicinal, decorative

Lady's Mantle

Alchemilla vulgaris

Native to Europe, this hardy plant thrives in a range of conditions, from damp grassland to mountain ledges. Its Latin name derives from the Arabic *alchimia*, meaning "alchemy," reflecting a belief in the plant's magical properties. Herbalists reputedly gathered the drops of early morning dew, which lay in the herb's fan-shaped leaves for use in potions. The common name is inspired by the characteristic mantle shape of the leaf and also reflects the ancient tradition of using this herb to treat women's menstrual problems. Medicinally, lady's mantle was also employed to treat bleeding wounds and as a heart tonic and diuretic. Its dried leaves are used in infusions. Today, it is often planted as an ornamental garden plant, as an edging for borders.

Other names: Bear's foot, lion's foot, nine hooks, Our Lady's mantle

Plant family: Rosaceae

Height: 12in (30cm)

Habit: Hardy perennial with fan-shaped, indented, toothed green leaves and clusters of small, yellow-green flowers

Habitat: Full sun to partial shade and rich soil

Uses: Medicinal

Jack-by-the-Hedge

Alliaria petiolata

Native to Europe and temperate Asia, this hardy herb grows well in damp, shady places, such as hedgerows and wood edges. Both the leaves and stalk emit an unmistakable garlic smell when crushed, hence its popular names "garlic mustard" or "hedge garlic." Historically, jack-by-the-hedge has long been used for both medicinal and culinary purposes. It was taken internally to treat bronchitis and asthma and applied externally to relieve bites and stings and to treat minor injuries. Believed to aid digestion, its young leaves were used as a potherb, adding a mild garlic flavor to soups or stews, or finely chopped and added to salads.

Other names: Garlic mustard, hedge garlic
Plant family: Brassicaceae
Height: 1–4ft (30cm–1.2m)
Habit: Hardy perennial with heart-shaped, toothed, bright green leaves and flat-topped clusters of small, white flowers
Habitat: Moist soil in shade or sun
Uses: Culinary, medicinal

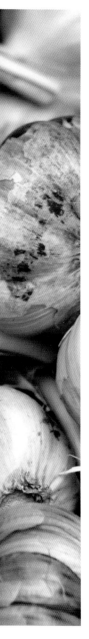

Garlic

Allium sativum

Mankind's use of garlic's strong-smelling bulbs goes back several millennia, making garlic one of the world's oldest herbs. Its use is chronicled in Babylonian times, over 5,000 years ago, while the Ancient Egyptians thought it imparted strength and the Ancient Romans ate it before going into battle. Thought to originate from Asia, garlic is widely grown and used around the world. It has historically been valued for its medicinal properties, with its first mention in Chinese traditional medicine around AD 500. Its antiseptic properties have long been recognized and its juice was extracted to treat the wounds of soldiers in World War I. Today, garlic is valued for its ability to reduce low-density lipoproteins ("bad" cholesterol) and is the subject of much scientific research. As a culinary herb, garlic is used in myriad ways, adding its full-bodied flavor to salad dressings, stews, curry pastes, pasta sauces, stir-fries, and many other dishes. There is much folklore attached to garlic, most famously that it warded off vampires.

Plant family: Liliaceae
Height: 16–24in (40–60cm)
Habit: Hardy perennial with long, narrow, flat green leaves and a spherical pink or white flowerhead
Habitat: Prefers full sun and rich, well-drained soil
Uses: Culinary, medicinal

Chives

Allium schoenoprasum

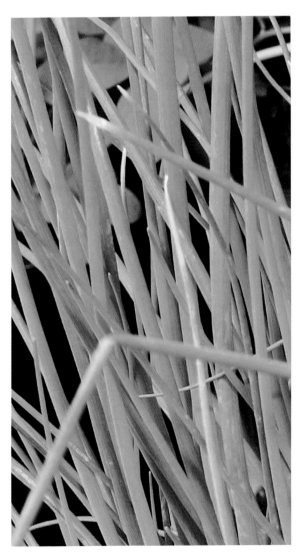

A well-known culinary herb, chives was introduced into Britain by the Romans. The common name is derived from the Latin *cepa*, which means "onion," a clue to its mild onion flavor. The Latin name is from *schoenus*, for "a rush or sedge," a reference to its reedlike appearance and during the Middle Ages it was called "rush-leek." Chives is used fresh and raw rather than cooked, particularly in egg dishes, such as omelets or scrambled eggs. Bright green, finely snipped chives is a popular garnish, sprinkled over soups or soured cream, for example. Both the leaves and the pretty, edible flowers can be added to salads. Medicinally, chives was valued for its stimulant effect on the appetite and as an aid to digestion.

Plant family: Liliaceae
Height: 9in (22.5cm)
Habit: Hardy perennial with long, slender, grasslike, green leaves and globular clusters of tiny, purple flowers
Habitat: Tolerant of most soils, with moist, well-drained soil ideal
Uses: Culinary, medicinal

Aloe Vera

Aloe vera (Aloe barbadensis)

Native to southern Africa, this architectural plant, with its striking foliage, is now a popular houseplant in countries with cooler climates. It has long been valued for its medicinal properties, with the Ancient Egyptians using it to treat catarrh. It was so prized that Alexander the Great is said to have conquered the island of Socotra in the Indian Ocean so that his soldiers could benefit from the wound-healing properties of the aloes growing on the island. Its succulent leaves contain a gel (obtained simply by breaking off a leaf and cutting it open), which can be spread directly on cuts and minor burns where it both soothes and stimulates the healing process. It is still valued medicinally, with the gel from its leaves being harvested and sold fresh or evaporated for use in creams, lotions, pills, and tinctures.

Other name: Barbados aloe
Plant family: Aloeaceae
Height: 2ft (60cm)
Habit: Tender perennial with rosettes of succulent gray-green, spiked, pointed foliage and bell-shaped, yellow, or orange flowers on a stem
Habitat: Sun and well-drained soil
Uses: Medicinal

35

Lemon Verbena

Aloysia triphylla

Introduced to Europe from Chile in the late eighteenth century, this citrus-scented herb has become a popular garden plant. It thrives best in its native South America, where it reaches impressive heights not attained in temperate climates. Its essential oil, with its strong lemon fragrance, has long been widely used in the perfume and cosmetics industry. As its dried leaves retain their fragrance well it is a popular component in potpourris. Medicinally, lemon verbena was valued for its mild sedative properties and for relieving spasms. As a culinary herb, its most common use is in refreshing lemon verbena tea, made from fresh or dried leaves. It can also be added to fish dishes, vinegars, jellies, soft drinks, and fruit salads.

Plant family: Verbenaceae
Height: 3–10ft (1–3m)
Habit: Half-hardy deciduous perennial with long, oval, green leaves and tiny, pale lilac to white flowers
Habitat: Prefers a sunny spot with light, well-drained soil
Uses: Culinary, medicinal, cosmetic

Marsh Mallow

Althaea officinalis

Found throughout Western Europe, Central Asia and North Africa, the marsh mallow, as its common name suggests, thrives in damp conditions and can cope with waterlogged soil, growing wild in marshland. Its generic name *Althaea* comes from the Greek word *altho*, "to cure," and it has a long history as a healing plant. The plant's high mucilage content, particularly present in the root, has softening and healing properties, and can be taken internally to treat coughs, sore throats, and stomach ulcers. In cosmetics, mallow is used as a soothing skin toner and a dry hair rinse. Valued by the Romans as a vegetable, its mucilaginous roots were once the basis for the confection marshmallow. The French traditionally eat its young leaves in salads to stimulate the kidneys.

Other names: Mortification root, sweet weed, white mallow
Plant family: Malvaceae
Height: 2–4ft (60–120cm)
Habit: Hardy perennial with velvety, toothed, lobed, green leaves and pink or white, five-petaled flowers
Habitat: Prefers full sun and light damp to wet soil
Uses: Culinary, medicinal, cosmetic

Dill

Anethum graveolens

This dainty herb derives its name from the Old Nordic *dilla*, meaning "to lull," with dill seed being one of the main ingredients in gripe water, used to soothe fretful babies. The seventeenth-century English herbalist Culpeper wrote of it being employed to treat flatulence and hiccups, and it was long regarded as a medicinal herb. Today, we think of it primarily as a culinary herb and use both its delicately flavored leaves and caraway-flavored seeds in the kitchen. Dill seeds are often an ingredient in pickles, especially dill pickles, and in cabbage dishes, such as sauerkraut and coleslaw. In Nordic countries, dill's clean, refreshing flavor is often added to cut through sour cream or yogurt.

Other names: Dillseed, dillweed
Plant family: Umbelliferae
Height: 2–3ft (60–90cm)
Habit: Hardy annual with fine, feathery, green fronds and flattened clusters of tiny, yellow flowers followed by buff-colored, oval seeds
Habitat: Prefers full sun and well-drained soil
Uses: Culinary, medicinal

Angelica

Angelica archangelica

As its name suggests, this large, handsome herb has long, but mysterious, heavenly associations. Medieval herbalists called it *herba angelica*, meaning "angelic plant," while Renaissance doctors named it "root of the Holy Ghost." One piece of folklore says that it flowers on May 8th, the feast day of Michael the Archangel, hence its name. Another legend tells of an angel who revealed the herb's protective qualities in a dream, and a piece of angelica root held in the mouth was thought to protect against the plague. Today, its fragrant essential oil is used in aromatherapy, perfumes, and colognes. While the seeds add flavor to Chartreuse liqueur, angelica is best-known in culinary terms for the use of its candied stalk and leaf stem in cake decoration.

Other names: Archangel, garden angelica, root of the Holy Ghost
Plant family: Umbelliferae
Height: 3–8ft (1–2.5m)
Habit: Hardy biennial with thick, hollow stalks, large, glossy, divided green leaves and globe-shaped clusters of tiny, yellow-green flowers
Habitat: Sun or partial shade and rich, moist soil
Uses: Culinary, cosmetic

Chervil

Anthriscus cerefolium

According to Pliny the Elder (writing in the first century AD) chervil was first cultivated in Syria. There it was eaten as a vegetable, but the Ancient Romans used it as a flavor-adding herb. During the Middle Ages it was valued for its medicinal qualities, prescribed to cleanse the liver and kidneys. Thought of as a "spring tonic" or cleansing herb, it was one of the herbs traditionally eaten during Lent. When it comes to culinary uses, chervil, with its delicate aniseed flavor, is best used fresh rather than dried. It is particularly valued in France where it is one of the traditional *fines herbes* (a mixture of chopped fresh herbs used in cooking) and features in Béarnaise or ravigote sauces.

Plant family: Umbelliferae
Height: 12–24in (30–60cm)
Habit: Hardy biennial (often grown as an annual) with hollow, lined stems, delicate, bright, lacy leaves and clusters of tiny, white flowers
Habitat: Partial shade and rich, moisture-retentive soil
Uses: Culinary, medicinal

Wild Celery

Apium graveolens

Native to Europe, North Africa, and South-West Asia, this hedgerow plant has a pronounced celery smell and a strong, bitter taste. It has been in use since ancient times and is mentioned in Ancient Egyptian texts and in Homer's *Odyssey*. The Latin name *graveolens*, meaning "strong-smelling," is a reference to its characteristic, highly aromatic scent. Because of its powerful taste it was used primarily as a flavoring. Cultivated celery, *Apium graveolens* var. *dulce*, with its milder flavor allowing it to be eaten as a vegetable, was developed from wild celery during the seventeenth century in France and Italy. Medicinally, wild celery was eaten to treat indigestion and loss of appetite and to reduce blood pressure.

Other name: Smallage
Plant family: Umbelliferae
Height: Up to 3ft (90cm)
Habit: Hardy biennial with solid, grooved stems, lobed and toothed green leaves, and clusters of tiny, green-white flowers
Habitat: Prefers full sun and rich, well-drained soil
Uses: Culinary, medicinal

Burdock

Arctium lappa

This tall, robust herb, native to Europe and West Asia but also found in North America, grows in waste ground and by roadsides. Its characteristic hooked burrs are the reason for its generic name, from the Greek *arktos* for "bear" and the Latin *lappa* meaning "burr." Traditionally popular with children for playing with, the burrs were nicknamed "beggar's buttons." There is a long history of using burdock medicinally, and in both Chinese and western medicine it was highly regarded as a blood-cleanser and detoxifier. In fact, it has been used to treat a wide range of conditions including eczema, measles, rheumatism, and gout. Its long, mucilaginous roots are edible and are highly prized in Japan, where cultivated burdock is called *gobo*. Its young stalks are also edible, either raw in salads or lightly boiled until tender.

Other names: Beggar's buttons, great burdock
Plant family: Asteraceae
Height: Up to 5ft (1.5m)
Habit: Hardy biennial with ovate to heart-shaped, green leaves and round, purple flowers
Habitat: Moist, neutral to alkaline soil in sun or light shade
Uses: Culinary, medicinal

Horseradish

Armoracia rusticana
(A. lapathifolia, Cochlearia armoracia)

Native to Eastern Europe and West Asia, horseradish is notoriously difficult to eradicate once established and consequently has naturalized throughout Europe and the United States. The plant has also long been cultivated for its leaves and its stout, white roots, both of which are edible. The English name "horseradish" derives from the word "hoarse" meaning coarse and strong and is a reference to its pungent odor and hot taste. During the Middle Ages, horseradish was used medicinally to aid digestion, as a diuretic and to treat urinary tract infections. In Europe the root also became popular as a condiment, mixed with vinegar, and served with fish or meat. In Britain a relish made from grated horseradish is traditionally served with roast beef. Because the large, fresh root deteriorates quickly once sliced, it is traditionally preserved in vinegar or as a pickle.

Plant family: Brassicaceae
Height: 1–4ft (30cm–1.2m)
Habit: Hardy perennial with long, green, oblong leaves and tiny, white flowers
Habitat: Well-drained, rich soil in sun or partial shade
Uses: Culinary, medicinal

Arnica

Arnica montana

Native to Europe and West Asia, this pretty, aromatic herb is an alpine species that grows wild in mountainous regions, thriving in cool conditions. Both its soft, downy leaves and its roots were smoked, leading to the nickname "mountain tobacco." For centuries, however, arnica has been best known for its healing properties in the treatment of bruises and sprains. It is also used to stimulate the immune system and the heart, with the German poet Goethe (1749–1832) reputed to have taken it for angina, and it remains a popular treatment for heart conditions in Germany today. Recent medical studies have questioned the safety of taking arnica internally. In homeopathic preparations, however, it is considered safe and is widely used.

Other names: Mountain tobacco, sneezewort, mountain arnica
Plant family: Asteraceae
Height: Up to 2ft (60cm)
Habit: Hardy perennial with oval, hairy, green leaves and orange-yellow, daisylike flowers
Habitat: Well-drained, humus-rich, sandy, acid soil in a sunny position
Uses: Medicinal

Southernwood

Artemisia abrotanum

Native to Southern Europe, this bushy shrub is nowadays primarily grown as a cultivated plant. Its strongly aromatic leaves repel moths and flies and it was a traditional component for nosegays. The French call it *garde-robe*, using it in their wardrobes to protect their clothes. Medicinally, this bitter herb was used to improve digestion and liver function and also to stimulate menstruation. The seventeenth-century herbalist Nicholas Culpeper attributed to southernwood the power of curing baldness, recommending that a paste made from its ashes be rubbed on the head to promote hair growth. In the kitchen, its strong, bitter taste meant it was added sparingly, traditionally to flavor cakes and vinegars in France and Italy, and its leaves can be mixed into salads.

Other names: Lad's love, old man
Plant family: Asteraceae
Height: Up to 3ft (90cm)
Habit: Semi-evergreen, hardy shrub with branching shoots covered with feathery, gray-green leaves and clusters of tiny, yellow flowers
Habitat: Well-drained soil in sunny position
Uses: Culinary, medicinal, decorative, insect repellent

Wormwood

Artemisia absinthium

Native to Europe and temperate Asia, wormwood grows naturally in waste places and on rocky hillsides. Since Ancient Egyptian times this notoriously bitter herb has been valued for its medicinal properties, considered to be a stimulating tonic. Its common name refers to its use in worming, and it was also used as a strewing herb and insect repellent. In the Bible the bitterness of wormwood is tellingly used as a metaphor for grim consequences: "But her end is bitter as wormwood" (Proverbs 5: 3–4). Essential oil of wormwood was a key ingredient in absinthe, an alcoholic apéritif invented in France in 1797. Addictive and fashionable, absinthe became notorious for its destructive effect upon those who drank it and was banned in 1915.

Other name: Absinthe
Plant family: Asteraceae
Height: Up to 3ft (90cm)
Habit: Semi-evergreen, hardy shrub with gray-green divided leaves and clusters of tiny, yellow flowers
Habitat: Well-drained, neutral to alkaline soil in sunny position
Uses: Medicinal, culinary

Tarragon

Artemisia dracunculus

With its distinctive aromatic flavor, with faint licorice overtones, French tarragon (as opposed to coarser-flavored Russian tarragon) is a popular culinary herb. It is particularly prized in French cuisine, where it is one of the *fines herbes* (a mixture of chopped fresh herbs). As well as to make tarragon vinegar, it also lends its name to various dishes, such as *oeufs en gelée à l'estragon*. It should be used fresh rather than dried, when its flavor is far more pronounced, and with discretion. Classically, tarragon is added to flavor chicken, egg, and fish dishes, such as Béarnaise sauce. As well as being prized for its flavor, tarragon was thought to be an aid against flatulence.

Other names: Estragon, French tarragon, little dragon
Plant family: Asteraceae
Height: Up to 3ft (90cm)
Habit: A bushy half-hardy perennial with long, slender, green leaves and sprays of tiny, yellow-gray flowers
Habitat: Well-drained soil in a sunny position
Uses: Culinary, medicinal

Mugwort

Artemisia vulgaris

Native to the northern temperate zone, mugwort grows in waste ground or on waysides. There is a venerable history of using mugwort medicinally; it is mentioned in Ancient Chinese medicinal lore and Greek and Roman writing, while the druids valued it as one of the nine herbs used to repel poison. Reputedly, Roman soldiers placed mugwort leaves in their sandals to help prevent tiredness on long marches. It was particularly known as a treatment for difficult or irregular menstruation and the menopause. Mugwort was known as the "mother of herbs" and has ancient associations with witchcraft and fertility rituals. In European cookery, mugwort's bitter flavor is used to cut through fatty foods, such as eel, goose, or duck.

Plant family: Asteraceae
Height: 2–5$\frac{1}{2}$ft (60cm–1.7m)
Habit: Hardy perennial with purplish stems and deeply cut, dark green leaves, and small, yellow or reddish-pink flowers
Habitat: Well-drained, neutral soil in a sunny position
Uses: Culinary, medicinal

Daisy

Bellis perennis

Native to Europe and Western Asia, the daisy is a very common grassland species, found in lawns and fields. It has long been regarded with affection for its appealing appearance, with its generic name *Bellis* meaning "pretty." The common name derives from the Old English "day's eye," referring to both the flower's appearance and the fact that it opens during daylight hours. In traditional medicine it was considered a wound herb, used to treat fresh wounds. Its other common name "bruisewort" refers to its use to relieve aches and bruises. In his *Herball* (1597) John Gerard writes of daisies offering relief from the pain of gout when applied in a poultice to the joints. In the kitchen, its young leaves, flower buds, and petals may be added to salads.

Other name: Bruisewort
Plant family: Asteraceae
Height: 1–6in (2.5–15cm)
Habit: Hardy perennial with rosettes of slightly toothed, oblong to ovate, green leaves and flowers consisting of a yellow disc surrounded by a fringe of several white or pink-flushed petals
Habitat: Well-drained soil in sun or partial shade
Uses: Culinary, medicinal

Borage

Borago officinalis

Native to the Mediterranean and western Asia, this sturdy plant grows naturally on waste ground and has long been cultivated in kitchen gardens. Since ancient times, borage has been regarded as having a heartening effect, with Robert Burton writing of it in his *Anatomy of Melancholy* (1621) as a good plant "to purge the veins of melancholy." Gerard, in his 1597 *Herball*, writes of borage leaves and flowers being added to wine to "make men and women merry." Young borage leaves, with their mild cucumber flavor, can be used in salads, egg mayonnaise, or soft cheese dips, while fresh borage tea is said to be useful against colds.

Other name: Starflower
Plant family: Boraginaceae
Height: Up to 2ft (60cm)
Habit: Hardy annual with lanceolate, hairy, green leaves and five-petaled, star-shaped, blue flowers
Habitat: Chalky to rich, well-drained soil in full sun
Uses: Culinary, medicinal

Calamint

Calamintha grandiflora

This hardy, aromatic plant is native to Europe, growing wild in hedgerows, woods, and along roadsides. In traditional medicine it was valued as an expectorant, while the seventeenth-century herbalist Culpeper recommended it for jaundice, nerves, convulsions, and "all afflictions of the brain." It was also known for causing abortions, containing as it does the active constituent pulegone. Its mint-scented leaves were traditionally used as a herb tea, made by steeping the fresh or dried leaves in boiling water, taken medicinally for weaknesses of the stomach or colic. Its ornamental appearance makes it an attractive addition to a herb garden.

Other name: Mint savory
Plant family: Lamiaceae
Height: 15in (37cm)
Habit: Hardy perennial with square stems, toothed, ovate, green leaves, and pink-purple flowers
Habitat: Well-drained to dry, neutral to alkaline soil in the sun
Uses: Medicinal, decorative

Marigold

Calendula officinalis

Native to Central Europe and the Mediterranean, the marigold is widely cultivated for medicinal, culinary, and ornamental purposes. Its generic name *Calendula* is derived from the Latin *Kalandae,* the first day of the month in the Roman calendar. Long noted for its healing, antiseptic, and detoxifying properties, the marigold has a venerable history of medicinal use, dating back to early Indian and Arabic cultures and also Ancient Greece and Rome. In the Middle Ages, the marigold was used to treat a range of ailments, including intestinal problems, smallpox, and measles. Externally, the plant was applied in the treatment of conjunctivitis, burns, and eczema. Marigold flowers are a traditional colorant, adding a yellow tint to cheese, butter, cakes, and rice dishes.

Other name: Pot marigold
Plant family: Asteraceae
Height: 20–28in (50–70cm)
Habit: Hardy annual with bright green, lanceolate leaves and yellow or orange flowers
Habitat: Well-drained soil in full sun
Uses: Culinary, medicinal, cosmetic, colorant

Lady's Smock

Cardamine pratensis

Native to Europe, North America, and North Asia, lady's smock grows wild in damp grasslands. Its common name "cuckoo flower" is thought to have come about because the plant flowers at the same time as the cuckoo arrives in Europe. Its generic name *Cardamine* derives from the Greek *kardamon*, meaning "cress," as the plant resembles watercress. It is traditionally thought of as a tonic cleansing herb. High in vitamin C, its edible leaves and flowers are traditionally eaten in salads. In Britain, lady's smock is a plant with much folklore attached to it, including the belief that it attracted adders. It was also thought that picking the flowers resulted in lightning and thunder.

Other names: Cuckoo flower, meadow cress
Plant family: Brassicaceae
Height: 12–18in (30–45cm)
Habit: Hardy perennial with a rosette of long-stalked, pinnate leaves and small, white, or lilac, four-petaled flowers
Habitat: Moist soil in sun or partial shade
Uses: Culinary, medicinal

Safflower

Carthamus tinctorius

Native to West Asia, this thistle-like plant was introduced into Europe from Egypt and is today widely cultivated around the world. The name *Carthamus* comes from the Arabic *qurtom* or the Hebrew *qarthami*, which mean "to paint," and was given to the safflower because its flowers yield orange and red dyes. It has a long history of being used as a coloring for fabrics and foods, mentioned for this purpose in Egypt in 3000 BC; and as a red pigment for silk and rouge. In cookery it was seen as a cheaper substitute for saffron, hence its common names "false saffron" or "saffron thistle." Today, safflower oil, extracted from the seeds, is valued as a cooking oil, high in polyunsaturates, and the plant is grown commercially for this purpose.

Other names: False saffron, saffron thistle, dyer's saffron
Plant family: Asteraceae
Height: 12–24in (30–60cm)
Habit: Hardy annual with dark green, spiny, lanceolate leaves and yellow or orange, thistle-like flowerheads
Habitat: Light, well-drained soil in the sun
Uses: Culinary, colorant

Caraway

Carum carvi

Indigenous to West Asia and the Mediterranean region, caraway is found growing wild in grassy fields and waste ground. It is cultivated for its small, brown, aromatic seeds, high in carvone, which gives them their characteristic strong, aniseed-like flavor and scent. Caraway has a long history of usage in the Middle East and was also used by the Ancient Egyptians. Although medicinally caraway is a traditional treatment for indigestion, with its seeds chewed to freshen breath and aid digestion, it has primarily been used in the kitchen. Introduced into Europe in the Middle Ages, caraway plays a large part particularly in German and East European cuisine, adding its distinctive flavor to sauerkraut, rye bread, sausages, cheese, cakes, and liqueurs such as kummel.

Plant family: Apiaceae
  (Umbelliferae)
Height: 2–3ft (60–90cm)
Habit: Hardy biennial with light
  green, feathery, fernlike leaves
  and clusters of tiny, white, or
  pinkish flowers
Habitat: Well-drained or heavy soil
  in full sun
Uses: Culinary, medicinal

Centaury

Centaurium erythraea

Native to Europe and South-West Asia, centaury grows naturally on dry grassland, sand dunes, and cliff edges. Its common name "centaury" is said to have derived from the Greek mythological figure of the centaur Chiron, half man, half horse, famous for his knowledge of herbal medicine, who reputedly used the herb. In ancient times, centaury was seen as a herb possessing magical properties, thought to be a universal purifier. It has a long history of being used to stimulate the appetite and improve digestion. It is an extremely bitter herb, but despite its off-putting taste was traditionally recommended for a variety of purposes, including killing worms, healing wounds, and nullifying adder venom. It is still employed today as an appetite stimulant.

Other names: Bitterherb, feverwort
Plant family: Gentianaceae
Height: Up to 10in (25cm)
Habit: Hardy biennial with basal rosette of wedge-shaped, green leaves and clusters of small, starlike, five-petaled, pink flowers
Habitat: Well-drained, sandy soil, ideally in full sun
Uses: Medicinal

Chamomile

Chamaemelum nobile

This low-growing, creeping herb is native to Western Europe and North America, growing wild on verges and waste ground. The generic name "*Chamaemelum*" comes from the Greek *chamaimelon*, meaning "ground apple," after the apple-like scent the plant gives off when crushed. High in aromatic oils, chamomile is little troubled by pests and indeed has been called a "physician plant," since it has a reputation for protecting sickly neighboring plants. During the Middle Ages this fragrant plant was a popular strewing herb for floors and there is a tradition of growing chamomile lawns for their scent. Medicinally, chamomile has long been a treatment for indigestion, with the dried flowers of *Chamaemelum nobile* used in herb teas.

Other names: Garden chamomile, Roman chamomile
Plant family: Asteraceae
Height: Up to 1ft (30cm)
Habit: Hardy, perennial evergreen with finely divided, green leaves and long-stalked, solitary flowers with yellow discs and fine, white petals
Habitat: Most soils, from full sun to light shade
Uses: Medicinal, culinary, decorative

Chicory

Cichorium intybus

Native to Europe and West Asia, chicory grows wild in hedgerows, fields, and on roadsides. Known to the Ancient Egyptians, Greeks, and Romans, chicory has long been an important herb, both medicinal and culinary. Medicinally, it was used for purging, to treat sore eyes, as a remedy for gallstones, and as a digestive. Its bitter leaves were picked when young and tender and used in salads and cultivated chicory was developed from it in the sixteenth century. Bitter chicory roots have long been roasted to use as an adulterant to coffee. Its leaves were also boiled to produce a blue dye. There is much folklore attached to the herb, including the legend that its blue flowers are the eyes of a girl crying for her sweetheart lost at sea.

Other name: Wild succory
Plant family: Asteraceae
Height: 3ft (90cm)
Habit: Hardy perennial with lance-shaped, toothed, mid-green leaves and purple-blue flowers
Habitat: Light, alkaline soil in sunshine
Uses: Culinary, medicinal, colorant

Winter Purslane

Claytonia perfoliata (Montana perfoliata)

Native to North America, winter purslane was introduced to Europe where it has since naturalized, and is found growing on dry soil along roadsides. The common name "miner's lettuce" can be traced back to the Gold Rush in California, when prospectors ate the fresh, green leaves of the plant in spring to help them prevent scurvy after the shortages of harsh winters. Its blossoms and fleshy leaves can be eaten in salads or the leaves can be cooked and eaten as a green vegetable.

Other name: Miner's lettuce
Plant family: Portulacaceae
Height: Up to 12in (30cm)
Habit: Hardy annual with perfoliate, green leaves (that is, encircling the stem) and small, white or pinkish, five-petaled flowers
Habitat: Light, fairly rich, free-draining soil in full sun
Uses: Culinary

Lily-of-the-Valley

Convallaria majalis

Native to Europe and North America, the lily-of-the-valley grows wild in woodland and meadows and has been widely cultivated. Its generic name is derived from the Latin *convallium*, meaning "of the valley," and *majalis*, referring to "May," the month in which this plant blooms. It is for its white, bell-like flowers, with their heady, fragrant scent, that the plant is best-known today and since the Middle Ages the flowers have symbolized modesty and purity. Historically, the plant was also valued for medicinal reasons, and despite all parts of it being poisonous, it was used as a tonic for weak hearts. Today, we know that the plant contains cardiac glycosides, which strengthen and regularize the heartbeat.

Other name: May lily
Plant family: Convallariaceae
Height: 6in (15cm)
Habit: Hardy perennial with mid-green, long, oval leaves and stems of white, bell-shaped flowers
Habitat: Moist soil in shade or semi-shade
Uses: Medicinal, decorative

Coriander

Coriandrum sativum

This aromatic annual, native to the eastern Mediterranean, is one of the oldest known herbs, cultivated for over 3,000 years, used by the Ancient Egyptians and Romans and mentioned in Sanskrit texts. Although the plant has medicinal applications in the treatment of indigestion, it is as a culinary herb that coriander is widely used all over the world. In India its fragrant seeds are a fundamental spice, used to flavor curries and other dishes, while its leaves are an ingredient in fresh chutneys. In Latin America its leaves flavor fish, meat, and poultry dishes, while in Thailand the whole plant, including its roots, is used in curry pastes. In French cookery, coriander seeds are essential for dishes *à la Grecque* while in Germany it flavors a range of different sausages.

Other names: Chinese parsley, cilantro
Plant family: Apiaceae
Height: 6–28in (15–70cm)
Habit: Hardy annual with finely cut, aromatic leaves and clusters of small, white flowers
Habitat: Moderately rich, well-drained soil in full sun to light shade
Uses: Culinary, medicinal

Lemongrass

Cymbopogon citratus

Native to Southeast Asia, this aromatic, tropical herb is today cultivated in many countries around the world. As its common name suggests, it has a distinctive lemon scent and flavor, due to its essential oil containing the constituent citral. Lemongrass is widely used in Southeast Asian cuisine, adding its fragrance to numerous dishes, including soups, curries, and sauces throughout the region. As lemongrass stalks are tough and fibrous, it is often simply crushed to release its aromatic oils and added whole. In cooking, fresh lemongrass is infinitely preferable to dried. It is also valued as an insect repellent (usually under its other name "citronella") and used as a skin cleanser, a tonic, and an aid to digestion.

Other name: Citronella
Plant family: Poaceae
Height: Up to 5ft (1.5m)
Habit: Tender, clump-forming perennial with dense stems and long, thin leaves
Habitat: Well-drained soil in sun with moderate humidity
Uses: Culinary, medicinal, cosmetic, insect repellent

Clove Pink

Dianthus caryophyllus

Native to Southern Europe and North Africa, the clove pink is the wild ancestor of the cultivated carnation, now grown throughout the world. Its generic name *Dianthus* comes from the Greek *dios* meaning "god" and *anthos* meaning "flower." The clove pink's pretty flowers, with their strong clove fragrance, have long been valued both for their appearance and their perfume, used by the Ancient Greeks and Romans for garlands. It is one of the oldest flowers to be cultivated in Britain. In traditional medicine it was mixed in tonic cordials to treat fevers. Culinarily, its petals were used to flavor vinegars, ales, sauces, and salads, adding a spicy, clovelike taste. Candied petals (with the bitter white part removed) were a popular cake decoration, while dried clove pink petals are found in potpourris.

Other names: Gillyflower, wild carnation
Plant family: Caryophyllaceae
Height: 8–20in (20–50cm)
Habit: Hardy, evergreen perennial with gray-green, lanceolate leaves and deep pink to purple flowers
Habitat: Well-drained, neutral to alkaline soil
Uses: Culinary, medicinal, decorative

Sundew

Drosera rotundifolia

Native to temperate Eurasia and North America, this hardy perennial is found growing in peat bogs, marshes, heaths, and moors, often among sphagnum moss. It is insectivorous, secreting a digestive enzyme, which attracts, catches, and dissolves insects. The generic name *Drosera* comes from the Greek *drosos*, meaning "dew," a reference to the droplets of enzyme on the plant's leaves. In traditional medicine the plant was used as a fortifying tonic and reputed to have aphrodisiac effects. Today, sundew is harvested from the wild for the plumbagin that it contains, active against a range of pathogenic bacteria. Sundew is also very popular with collectors of carnivorous plants.

Other name: Dewplant
Plant family: Droseraceae
Height: 4–6in (10–15cm)
Habit: Hardy perennial with a
   rosette of red-green, sticky,
   spoon-shaped leaves and small,
   white, five-petaled flowers
Habitat: Wet peat in sun
Uses: Medicinal, decorative

65

Echinacea

Echinacea purpurea

Native to North America, this attractive herb grows wild in woodlands but is today cultivated in a number of countries. The name "echinacea" comes from the Greek *echinos*, meaning "hedgehog," a small, spiny European mammal, referring to its flower's prickly cone. Its medicinal properties were first discovered by Native Americans, who used a number of echinacea species to treat snake bites and infected wounds. There has been considerable research into the herb and it has been discovered that echinacea stimulates the body's immune system. Today, it is widely used as a herbal medicine, taken particularly to treat and prevent the common cold and influenza.

Other name: Purple coneflower
Plant family: Asteraceae
Height: Up to 5ft (1.5m)
Habit: Hardy perennial with large, hairy, ovate leaves and purple-pink, daisylike flowers with orange central cones
Habitat: Most soils in full sun or light shade
Uses: Medicinal

Viper's Bugloss

Echium vulgare

Native to Europe, viper's bugloss grows on waste ground, in uncultivated fields and by roadsides and is now naturalized throughout the northern hemisphere, indeed considered an invasive weed by many. The generic name derives from the Greek *ekios*, meaning "viper," thought to be because its seeds resemble snakes' heads. Appropriately, this herb was indeed used to treat snake bites in medieval times. In the seventeenth century Nicholas Culpeper wrote of it: "It is a herb of the sun. It is an especial remedy against both poisonous bites and poisonous herbs." Its juice was also applied to smooth, sensitive skin and to treat boils. Its young leaves can be eaten in salads.

Other names: Snakeflower, viper's grass
Plant family: Boraginaceae
Height: 2–4ft (60–120cm)
Habit: Hardy biennial with mid-green, hairy, oblong to lanceolate leaves, and funnel-shaped flowers that turn from pink to blue
Habitat: Light, dry soil in full sun
Uses: Culinary, medicinal

California Poppy

Eschscholzia californica

Native to western North America, this attractive plant grows in grassy, open areas and has naturalized in many other countries. A drought-tolerant, self-seeding herb, it thrives on disturbed land, often recolonizing after fires. Its generic name is after the nineteenth-century doctor and naturalist, Johann Friedrich von Eschscholtz. The California poppy was long used by Native Americans both as a food and as a medicine, eaten as a green vegetable, and applied in the treatment of toothaches and to kill lice. It is a plant with mild sedative and analgesic properties and continues to be used for these, particularly for treating children.

Plant family: Papaveraceae
Height: 3–4in (7–10cm)
Habit: Hardy annual with finely cut, blue-green leaves and four-petaled, yellow to orange flowers
Habitat: Well-drained to poor soil in full sun
Uses: Medicinal, culinary

Eucalyptus

Eucalyptus globulus

Native to Australia, the eucalyptus is grown in other temperate countries to reclaim marshy land, as a windbreak, and for ornamental purposes. Its aromatic oil (high in cineole, which has the characteristic eucalyptus scent) has long been used medicinally. As it possesses expectorant and decongestant properties, it is made into inhalations and vapor rubs to treat bronchitis, catarrh, colds, influenza, and sinusitis. Eucalpytus is a traditional flavoring for lozenges, taken to ease coughing. Effective against many bacteria, it is applied externally in liniments to treat bruises, sprains, and muscular pains and in ointments for wounds and abscesses. Eucalyptus oil, however, must be used only as recommended, as large doses of the essential oil can cause headaches and convulsions and may prove fatal.

Other names: Blue gum, Tasmanian blue gum

Plant family: Myrtaceae

Height: Up to 148ft (45m)

Habit: Tender tree with creamy white to gray bark that peels off in long, ribbon-like shreds, and long, lanceolate, silvery blue leaves

Habitat: Well-drained soil in sun

Uses: Medicinal, decorative

Joe Pye Weed

Eupatorium purpureum

Native to North America, Joe Pye weed grows wild in rich, swampy ground and damp ditches. Its common name is in honor of a Native American doctor from New England who used the plant to successfully treat typhus. The common name "boneset" comes about because of its use to treat bonebreak or dengue fever throughout America. It was also used medicinally to treat kidney stones, urinary disorders, such as cystitis, and painful menstruation. Its numerous flowers attract butterflies, bees, and other insect pollinators and make it a popular plant for garden borders.

Other names: Gravelroot, purple boneset

Plant family: Asteraceae

Height: 4–10ft (1.2–3m)

Habit: Hardy, clump-forming perennial with serrated, ovate, green leaves and clumps of small, pink, purplish, or white flowers

Habitat: Moist soil in sun or partial shade

Uses: Medicinal, decorative

Meadowsweet

Filipendula ulmaria (Spiraea ulmaria)

Native to Europe and West Asia, meadowsweet grows wild in fens, marshes, and meadows and on river banks. The common name derives from the Anglo-Saxon term "meadwort," that is a herb (wort) used to flavor mead. It has a long history of use by mankind and is said to be sacred to the druids. Its highly scented, creamy-white flowers made it a popular strewing herb during the Middle Ages and it was also traditionally used in churches for weddings, hence the name "bridewort." Medicinally, it was given as a diuretic and to treat heartburn, gastritis, and peptic ulcers. Culinarily, meadowsweet adds a delicious fragrance to vinegar and herbal beers and liqueurs.

Other names: Bridewort, queen of the meadows

Plant family: Rosaceae

Height: 2–4ft (60cm–1.2m)

Habit: Hardy perennial with pinnate, toothed leaves, divided into pairs of leaflets and clusters of tiny, creamy-white flowers

Habitat: Rich, moist to wet soil in sun or partial shade

Uses: Culinary, medicinal, decorative

Fennel

Foeniculum vulgare

Native to Southern Europe, wild fennel grows in wasteland and dry, sunny spots, particularly sea cliffs. It is an aromatic plant, with a distinctive anise-like flavor and scent, long used both medicinally and culinarily. Cultivated since ancient times, there are a number of varieties, with wild fennel noticeably bitter. In Greek mythology, Prometheus hid the fire he stole from the gods to bring to humanity in a hollow fennel stalk. The Romans ate fennel shoots as a vegetable and used the small, gray-brown seeds as a flavoring for sauces. Medicinally, fennel is noted as an aid to digestion, with fennel seeds prescribed for stomach pains, flatulence, and loss of appetite. Fennel tea is a traditional remedy for babies' colic.

Other name: Bitter fennel
Plant family: Apiaceae
Height: 4–7ft (1.5–2.1m)
Habit: Hardy to half-hardy biennial or perennial with bright green, feathery leaves and clusters of tiny, yellow flowers
Habitat: Well-drained, neutral to alkaline soil in full sun
Uses: Culinary, medicinal, decorative

Wild Strawberry

Fragaria vesca

Native to Europe, West Asia, and North America, the wild strawberry grows in forests, clearings, and by roadsides. Since ancient times it has been prized for its tiny but exquisitely flavored red fruit. Its generic name derives from the Latin *fragrans*, meaning "fragrant," a reference to its perfumed fruit. It has also long been used medicinally, taken to treat anaemia, kidney, and liver complaints and gout. Wild strawberry leaf tea is said to be a good tonic. Strawberries were also used cosmetically, to combat wrinkles and soothe sunburn. Because of their low yield and fragile fruit, wild strawberries are not widely cultivated. The strawberries generally available commercially are descended from two American species, which bore larger fruit.

Other name: Wood strawberry
Plant family: Rosaceae
Height: 10–12in (25–30cm)
Habit: Hardy, rosette-forming perennial with long runners and coarsely toothed, bright green, trifoliate leaves, and four or five white-petaled flowers with yellow centers
Habitat: Rich, neutral to alkaline soil in sun or partial shade
Uses: Culinary, medicinal

Goat's Rue

Galega officinalis

Native to Europe, goat's rue grows wild by streams and ponds and is also widely cultivated. The herb's generic name *Galega* comes from the Greek *gala*, meaning "milk," because the plant was reputed to increase milk yield, a fact that has been borne out by scientific research. In traditional herbalism, goat's rue, which promotes sweating, treated fever, the plague, and snake bites. It has also been used to lower blood sugar levels and to treat diabetes.

Other name: French lilac
Plant family: Papilionaceae
Height: 3–5ft (1–1.5m)
Habit: Hardy perennial with pinnate leaves with six to eight pairs of bright green, lanceolate leaflets, and lavender to white flowers
Habitat: Moist, well-drained soil in sun or partial shade
Uses: Medicinal

Sweet Woodruff

Galium odoratum

Native to Europe, North Africa, and Russia, sweet woodruff, with its fragrant flowers, grows in shady woodland and hedgerows. Dried sweet woodruff has a delicious odor of hay, honey, and vanilla and was highly prized in medieval times as a strewing herb. It was also used to scent linen chests and ward off moths and in potpourri, snuffs, and perfumery. Medicinally, it has been employed in the treatment of menstrual pains and varicose veins and as a sedative. In Germany, sweet woodruff is steeped in Rhine wine to create a delicately perfumed drink called *Maibowle*, drunk each year to celebrate May Day.

Other name: Master of the wood
Plant family: Rubiaceae
Height: 6in (15cm)
Habit: Hardy perennial with quadrangular stems, whorls of lanceolate, green leaves, and starshaped, white flowers
Habitat: Moist, well-drained, neutral to alkaline soil in shade
Uses: Medicinal, culinary, insect repellent

Lady's Bedstraw

Galium verum

Native to Europe, West Asia, and North America, lady's bedstraw grows widely in the wild, found in wasteland, sandy grassland, and by roadsides. The generic name *Galium* derives from the Greek *gala*, meaning "milk," thought to refer to its traditional use to curdle milk in cheesemaking, a quality made clear in its common name "cheese rennet." It was believed to promote sleep and used to stuff bedding, and in Christian legend was one of the herbs placed in baby Jesus's cradle in Bethlehem. Lady's bedstraw had numerous, traditional medicinal uses: as a diuretic, against epilepsy, and to treat skin complaints. It was also employed in dyeing, with its roots giving a red dye popularly used for tartan in Scotland.

Other names: Cheese rennet, yellow bedstraw
Plant family: Rubiaceae
Height: 6–39in (15cm–1m)
Habit: Hardy perennial with quadrangular stems, whorls of lanceolate, green, linear leaves, and tiny, yellow flowers
Habitat: Well-drained, neutral to alkaline soil in sun
Uses: Culinary, medicinal, colorant

Gardenia

Gardenia augusta

Native to China, Japan, Taiwan, and Vietnam, the gardenia is now widely cultivated. The plant's generic name is in honor of a noted eighteenth-century botanist, Dr. Alexander Garden. The gardenia has a venerable history of medicinal use in China, mentioned in traditional medicinal texts during the Han dynasty (AD 25–220). It is used to treat feverish colds and coughs, and diabetes, to check bleeding, and also to aid liver function. Taken externally, it is applied to wounds, sprains, and inflamed skin. Its edible fruit is used as a coloring in Japan and China, while its flowers flavor tea. In the West, it is admired for its attractive, fragrant blossoms and glossy foliage and found in bouquets, wreaths, and corsages.

Other name: Cape jasmine
Plant family: Rubiaceae
Height: 6½–40ft (2–12m)
Habit: Tender, evergreen shrub with glossy, dark green, ovate to elliptic leaves, and large, white flowers
Habitat: Well-drained, humus-rich, sandy, neutral to acid soil in light or partial shade
Uses: Medicinal, decorative, colorant

Wintergreen

Gaultheria procumbens

Native to the United States and Canada, wintergreen is an aromatic, creeping, evergreen shrub, which grows in the wild in cool, damp forests. It was long used by the Native Americans to treat aches and pains and to aid breathing. Oil of wintergreen, extracted from the plant, contains methyl salicylate, which gives the plant its distinctive medicinal scent. The oil has long had medicinal applications and has also been added as a flavoring for confectionery, cough drops, and toothpaste. Wintergreen tea, made from both the leathery leaves and from the berries, was a popular tonic while its red berries can be eaten raw or cooked in jams and jellies, or pies.

Other names: Checkerberry, creeping wintergreen, teaberry
Plant family: Ericaceae
Height: 3–6in (7–15cm)
Habit: Hardy, evergreen, perennial shrub, with glossy, dark green, ovate to elliptical leaves, and drooping, white, waxy flowers
Habitat: Moist, peaty, neutral to acid soil in partial shade
Uses: Medicinal, culinary

Yellow Gentian

Gentiana lutea

Native to Central and Southern Europe, yellow gentian is found growing in pastures in mountains such as the Alps and the Apennines. The generic name is in honor of King Gentius of Illyria (*c.* 500 BC), who is said to have discovered the plant's medicinal uses. Its common name "bitterwort," meaning "bitter leaf," reflects the plant's intensely bitter taste. So bitter is it that it can be detected when diluted to 1 in 12,000 parts. For centuries the plant's roots have been used to make tonics, taken to treat loss of appetite, indigestion, liver complaints, and gastric infections. Today, it flavors gentian liqueurs and Angostura bitters.

Other name: Bitterwort
Plant family: Gentianaceae
Height: 3–6ft (1–2m)
Habit: Hardy perennial with green, oval leaves and yellow, narrow-petaled flowers
Habitat: Moist, light, well-drained neutral to acid soil in sun or partial shade
Uses: Medicinal, culinary

Witch Hazel

Hamamelis virginiana

Native to the eastern states of North America, the deciduous shrub witch hazel grows in woodland but is also cultivated in America and Europe. The common name is thought to refer to the belief that the plant had magical powers, associated with witchcraft and with its forked twigs, used as divining rods. It has long been used medicinally by Native Americans, who made ointments and infusions from its leaves and twigs to treat sprains, aching muscles, and bruises. It is an astringent herb that checks bleeding and reduces inflammation, and distilled witch hazel is widely used around the world to treat minor skin ailments. Its pretty, late-season flowers, with their fragrant scent, have made it an attractive plant for backyards.

Other names: Snapping hazel, striped alder, winterbloom, American witch hazel

Plant family: Hamamelidaceae

Height: 15ft (5m)

Habit: Hardy shrub with broadly ovate, green leaves, which turn yellow in the fall, and clusters of two to four flowers with crinkled, yellow petals

Habitat: Moist, humus-rich, neutral to acid soil in sun or partial shade

Uses: Medicinal, decorative

Curry Plant

Helichrysum italicum (H. angustifolium)

Native to Southern Europe, the curry plant grows in dry, sunny places and is known primarily as a cultivated subshrub. Its silver-gray leaves give off a distinctive, spicy fragrance when brushed against, particularly after rain, hence its popular name. Its actual flavor is less strong than its scent, and it is used sparingly in cooking, with a few leaves being added to mayonnaise, cream cheese, and salads, or a sprig tucked into a roast chicken. With its scented, silvery foliage and yellow flowers, it is grown today mainly as an ornamental garden plant.

Plant family: Asteraceae
Height: 2ft (60cm)
Habit: Frost-hardy, evergreen
  subshrub with silver-gray,
  linear leaves, and small, yellow,
  buttonlike flowers
Habitat: Light, well-drained soil
  in sun
Uses: Culinary, decorative

St. John's Wort

Hypericum perforatum

Native to Europe and West Asia, St. John's wort grows wild in open woods, grassland and waste ground. It is traditionally associated with St. John the Baptist and has for centuries been highly regarded for its medicinal properties. Long used internally to treat nervous disorders and externally for healing, modern research has found it to contain the anti-depressants hypericin and hyperforin and to be a potent anti-viral. Today, it is a popular herbal remedy, taken for the treatment of anxiety or mild depression and applied externally to bruises, burns, and wounds. It is used fresh or dried to make creams, infusions, liquid extracts, medicinal oils, and tinctures. Easy to cultivate, it is a picturesque addition to a herb garden.

Other names: Grace of God, herb of St. John
Plant family: Guttiferae
Height: 2–3ft (60–90cm)
Habit: Hardy perennial with small, stalkless, ovate leaves and yellow, star-shaped, five-petaled flowers
Habitat: Well-drained to dry soil in sun or partial shade
Uses: Medicinal, decorative

Hyssop

Hyssopus officinalis

Native to Europe, West Asia, and North Africa, this aromatic herb grows wild on dry, rocky slopes and walls. The generic name *Hyssopus* is derived from the Hebrew *ezob*, which means "holy herb." A herb called hyssop is mentioned in the Old Testament, used for purification, although there are doubts as to whether this was *Hyssopus officinalis*. In traditional medicine, it was given to soothe chest complaints, coughs, and colds, with the seventeenth-century herbalist Nicholas Culpeper recommending it boiled with figs as a gargle. Its strongly aromatic, slightly bitter leaves and flowers were also added to salads, soups, casseroles, and sausages, though sparingly. It is the main flavoring of Chartreuse liqueur and is also used in making eau de cologne.

Other name: Blue hyssop
Plant family: Lamiaceae
Height: 18–24in (45–60cm)
Habit: Hardy, semi-evergreen perennial with lance-shaped leaves arranged in whorls and spikes of tubular, blue, pink, purple, or white flowers
Habitat: Well-drained, neutral to alkaline soil in the sun
Uses: Culinary, medicinal, cosmetic

Elecampane

Inula helenium

Native to Europe and West Asia, elecampane grows wild in fields and waste ground, but is usually cultivated. It has a long history of being used medicinally. Pliny wrote that the Roman Emperor Augustus declared "Let no day pass without eating some of the roots of enula [elecampane], considered to help digestion as well as mirth." Traditionally, its thick roots were infused to soothe coughs, sore throats, and bronchitis, to aid digestion and as a general tonic. It was also used to treat skin complaints, hence its common name of "scabwort." Candied elecampane root was a popular medicinal sweetmeat from the Middle Ages to the twentieth century, taken for chest complaints and asthma. With its tall, erect stems and large, cheerful, yellow flowers it is a popular addition to garden borders.

Other names: Elf dock, horse-heal, scabwort
Plant family: Asteraceae
Height: 10ft (3m)
Habit: Hardy perennial with pointed, slightly toothed, green leaves and large, bright yellow flowerheads
Habitat: Moist, well-drained soil in sun
Uses: Medicinal, decorative

Orris

Iris germanica var. *florentina*

Native to the Eastern Mediterranean, orris grows in the wild but is primarily a cultivated plant. The Greek word *iris*, meaning "rainbow," is possibly a reference to the plant family's varied, colored flowers. Since ancient times, orris has been highly prized for its violet-scented roots, used in its dried form by the Ancient Egyptians, Greeks, and Romans for unguents and perfumes. Medicinally, despite being toxic if eaten, orris was a treatment for coughs and diarrhea. The iris flower is the origin of the fleur-de-lis and has been associated with the Italian city of Florence since the early Middle Ages. Today, the plant is cultivated in parks and gardens for its attractive appearance, while its root and essential oil are ingredients in cosmetics and a variety of different candy.

Plant family: Iridaceae
Height: 2–4ft (60–120cm)
Habit: Hardy perennial with blade-shaped, green leaves and large, white, violet-tinged flowers
Habitat: Well-drained, neutral to alkaline soil in sun
Uses: Culinary, medicinal, cosmetic, decorative

Juniper

Juniperus communis

A conifer growing widely as either a shrub or small tree around the northern hemisphere, from the Mediterranean to North America, the juniper plant is valued for its aromatic berries. Probably their best-known use is as a flavoring for gin, the clear, spirit-based drink first made by the Dutch in the sixteenth century. The Dutch name for juniper, "*jenever*," led to it being called "geneva," from which the English derived the name "gin." Long before its use in gin, juniper had been valued for its medicinal qualities, employed by both the Ancient Egyptians and Greeks and in Indian Ayurvedic medicine. Dutch geneva was in fact first developed as a remedy for kidney disorders and today juniper is still used in herbal medicine.

Plant family: Cupressaceae
Height: 1–26ft (30cm–8m)
Habit: Hardy evergreen perennial, with small, green, pointed, needle-like leaves and small berries, dark blue-black when ripe
Habitat: Chalky soil on heaths, moorlands, mountain slopes, and in coniferous forests
Uses: Medicinal, culinary

Bay

Laurus nobilis

Revered by both the Ancient Greeks and the Romans, the bay tree has an impressive and venerable history. Sacred to the Greek sun-god Apollo, patron of music and poetry, the bay was used to make the laurel wreaths that crowned emperors, generals, and athletes. This use is reflected in its Latin name, with *laurus* meaning "praise" and *nobilis* meaning "renowned." In cooking, bay leaves are added fresh or dried and it is one of the herbs in a classic French *bouquet garni* (bundle of herbs). Bay leaves add their spicy flavor to a wide range of dishes, from stews and pasta sauces to pickled fish and marinated olives. Other historic uses of bay were as a strewing herb, to deter insects, and to treat indigestion.

Other names: Bay laurel, sweet bay, sweet laurel

Plant family: Lauraceae

Height: Up to 59ft (18m)

Habit: An evergreen tree with smooth, glossy, dark green, pointed, oval leaves and tiny, pale yellow flowers, followed by purple-black berries

Habitat: Prefers full sun to moderate shade and tolerates most soils

Uses: Culinary, medicinal

Lavender

Lavandula angustifolia

Long appreciated for its fragrant, scented leaves and flowers, lavender is nowadays an extensively cultivated herb. Commercial growers in France produce it on a large scale for its essential oil, used to scent perfumes, soaps, and oils, and it is also a popular garden plant, attracting bees and butterflies. The Ancient Greeks and Romans added lavender to their bathwater, both for its fragrance and for its therapeutic properties, hence its Latin name, from the Latin *lavare*, meaning "to wash." Thought to deter insects such as moths, lavender was employed as a strewing herb and to scent linen closets. Indeed, to this very day, small, pretty sachets of lavender are sold to scent wardrobes and drawers. In its infusion form, lavender has a sedative, calming effect and, in aromatherapy, lavender oil is used as a treatment for headaches and reducing tension. When it comes to the kitchen, lavender is not widely used, though sometimes it flavors sugar, syrups, and vinegar.

Other name: English lavender
Plant family: Lamiaceae
Height: Up to 3ft (90cm)
Habit: A hardy perennial with narrow, gray-green leaves and spikes of purple flowers
Habitat: Prefers full sun and well-drained soil
Uses: Culinary, medicinal, cosmetic, insect repellent

Cress

Lepidium sativum

Native to West Asia, cress is widely cultivated for its edible, peppery foliage. In Ayurvedic medicine, cress is used to treat a range of conditions, including indigestion, coughs, asthma, and rheumatic pain. In the West, however, it is regarded primarily as a culinary herb. A fast-growing plant, cress is grown from seed and the shoots are cut and eaten fresh at seedling stage. In Britain, cress seed is classically mixed with mustard seed to grow "mustard and cress," a traditional addition to egg mayonnaise sandwiches. Its fresh leaves can also be added to omelets, salads, soups, and herb butters and it is a traditional garnish.

Other names: Broad-leafed cress
Plant family: Brassicaceae
Height: 8–16in (20–40cm)
Habit: Hardy annual with linear to pinnate, green leaves and white, four-petaled flowers
Habitat: Well-drained soil in sun or partial shade
Uses: Culinary, medicinal

Lovage

Levisticum officinale

Native to the Mediterranean, lovage grows wild in mountain pastures and by streams. In medieval times it was called *luvesche* and *loveach*, and it has a long tradition of being used in aphrodisiacs. It was a popular flavoring herb in Ancient Greece and Rome, mentioned by the Roman epicure Apicius, and continued to be widely grown in kitchen gardens during medieval times. Medicinally, its aromatic seeds were chewed to aid digestion. Infusions of the root were recommended for jaundice and urinary problems and its fragrant leaves were valued for their deodorizing and antiseptic properties. Today, it is seen primarily as a culinary herb. Similar to celery, but with a milder flavor, lovage leaf-stalks and stem-bases can be blanched and eaten and its chopped leaves added to soups or salads, or cooked as a green vegetable.

Other names: Love parsley, sea parsley
Plant family: Apiaceae
Height: 6ft (2m)
Habit: Hardy perennial with green, divided leaves and tiny, greenish-yellow flowers
Habitat: Deep, rich, moist soil in sun or partial shade
Uses: Culinary, medicinal

Honeysuckle

Lonicera periclymenum

Found throughout the northern hemisphere, honeysuckle in the wild grows in hedgerows and woodland but is also extensively cultivated. Its common name is said to derive from the custom of sucking the sweet nectar from its flowers. Its exquisite fragrance has long made it a prized plant and today there are many cultivars available to gardeners. Medicinally, it was used as an expectorant, an antiseptic, and a diuretic. The sixteenth-century herbalist John Gerard mentioned the plant in his *Herball*, writing that its flowers steeped in oil were a good "anointment for cold bodies." Because of its heady perfume it has many associations with love and marriage. The scented flowers are used for potpourri, herb pillows, and cosmetics.

Other names: Bindweed, woodbine
Plant family: Caprifoliaceae
Height: Up to 30ft (10m)
Habit: Hardy, deciduous perennial
climber with paired, ovate, green
leaves and yellow, trumpet-
shaped flowers
Habitat: Well-drained soil in sun or
partial shade
Uses: Medicinal, cosmetic,
decorative

Purple Loosestrife

Lythrum salicaria

Native to Europe, Asia, and North Africa, purple loosestrife thrives in wetlands and marshy places. The generic name *Lythrum* comes from the Greek *lythron*, meaning "blood," thought to refer either to the bloodlike color of the flowers or its beneficial effects on the body. It has a long history of being used medicinally, with the seventeenth-century herbalist Nicholas Culpeper recommending it, particularly to treat eye infections. As purple loosestrife controls bleeding, it was used externally for wounds and sores and to treat internal bleeding, excessive menstrual flow, and nosebleeds. Scientific research has shown that it is effective against the bacteria that cause typhus and other feverish diseases.

Plant family: Lythraceae
Height: 2–5ft (60cm–1.5m)
Habit: Hardy perennial with lanceolate, green leaves and spikes of pink-purple flowers
Habitat: Moist, neutral to alkaline soil or shallow water in sun or partial shade
Uses: Medicinal

Lemon Balm

Melissa officinalis

With its distinctive lemon scent when its leaves are rubbed, lemon balm is a fragrant and easy-to-grow addition to the garden. Beloved by bees, its generic name derives from the Greek *melissa*, meaning "honey bee." For centuries, lemon balm has been valued for various medicinal properties, with the Romans considering it a useful aid for reviving spirits. Brought over to Britain by the Romans, it was a popular herb in monastery gardens, used for refreshing teas and ointments. Its anti-melancholy associations have continued over the centuries. Today, it is used in aromatherapy to treat depression. Its culinary uses are in tisanes (with lemon balm and peppermint a popular combination), dressings, custard, fruit salads, and jellies.

Other names: Balm, melissa
Plant family: Lamiaceae
Height: 12–24 in (30–60 cm)
Habit: A hardy perennial with toothed, oval almost heart-shaped, light green leaves and small, yellow-white flowers
Habitat: Prefers full sun or light shade in rich soil
Uses: Culinary, medicinal

Pennyroyal

Mentha pulegium

Native to Europe and North Africa, pennyroyal is a creeper, cultivated particularly for aromatic ground cover and to deter ants, and so often grown between paving stones. As with other members of the mint family, it is easy to grow and can be invasive. The name *pulegium* is derived from the Latin *pulex*, meaning "flea" because the plant's coarse, pungent scent was used to repel fleas and other pests, such as mice. Its leaves can be rubbed on bare skin to act as an insect deterrent and, medicinally, its oil can trigger abortions. The Elizabethan herbalist John Gerard recommended that its leaves be added to water on sea voyages to purify it. In England and Spain, pennyroyal was a traditional flavoring for sausages.

Other name: Pudding grass
Plant family: Lamiaceae
Height: 4–8in (10–20cm)
Habit: Hardy perennial with elliptic to ovate, bright green leaves and small, purple flowers
Habitat: Rich, moist soil in sun or partial shade
Uses: Culinary, medicinal, insect repellent

Peppermint

Mentha x piperita

A cross between spearmint and water mint, peppermint has a pronounced aroma and flavor. The menthol in peppermint gives the herb its characteristic effect when eaten, that is, an initial hotness followed by coolness in the mouth. This has made peppermint oil a popular ingredient in toothpastes, confectionery, such as chewing gum and mint sweets, and aftershaves. When it comes to cooking, peppermint oil rather than fresh peppermint leaves is used. Like other mints, peppermint is valued for its digestive and mouth-freshening qualities and peppermint sweets are often eaten after a meal. It is also considered to be an effective antispasmodic, a decongestant, and an antiseptic agent. As with other mints, peppermint is very easy to cultivate and should be grown in a pot to contain its invasive tendencies.

Plant family: Lamiaceae
Height: Up to 3ft (90cm)
Habit: Hardy perennial with purple-tinged, dark green, lanceolate leaves, and small, pale purple flowers
Habitat: Damp light soil in sun or partial shade
Uses: Culinary, medicinal

Spearmint

Mentha spicata

Spearmint, one of the best-known mints, has long been prized for its refreshing scent and flavor. In Greek mythology, Minthe was the name of a nymph transformed into the fragrant herb by the goddess of the Underworld. Introduced by the Romans to Britain, spearmint remains a popular herb to this very day. In British cookery it has a number of uses, adding flavor to new potatoes and peas or to make mint sauce or jelly, a classic accompaniment for roast lamb. A hardy plant, it is very easy to grow; indeed, it can become an invasive nuisance if not contained in a pot. Spearmint was historically valued for its digestive and mouth-freshening qualities and mint tea is served after meals throughout the Middle East. During the Middle Ages, it was used as a strewing herb and to deter rats and mice from grain stores.

Other name: Garden mint
Plant family: Lamiaceae
Height: Up to 3ft (90cm)
Habit: Hardy perennial with
     spearhead-shaped leaves and
     sprigs of tiny, pale purple, pink,
     or white flowers
Habitat: Damp, light soil in sun or
     partial shade
Uses: Culinary, medicinal, repellent

Bergamot

Monarda didyma

Native to North America, this attractive, flowering perennial grows wild in woodlands and by streams and is also a popular cultivated, ornamental garden plant. The common name "bergamot" is in tribute to its scent, similar to that of bergamot orange, while "bee balm" is thought to refer to the plant's appeal to bees and other pollinating insects, drawn by its fragrant, nectar-rich flowers. The plant's medicinal properties were well known by Native American tribes, who extracted and inhaled its oil to soothe bronchial complaints. They also made bergamot tea, known as Oswego tea after the Oswego Indians. Culinarily, its leaves and flowers can be used sparingly in salads, stuffings, lemonade, and sauces.

Other names: Bee balm, oswego tea

Plant family: Lamiaceae

Height: 16–48in (40cm–120cm)

Habit: Hardy perennial with dark green, ovate to lanceolate, coarsely toothed, rough-textured leaves and bright red, claw-shaped flowers

Habitat: Rich, moist soil in sun

Uses: Culinary, medicinal, decorative

Sweet Cicely

Myrrhis odorata

Native to Europe, sweet cicely grows wild in meadows, woods, and hedges. The specific name *odorata* comes from the Latin *odorus*, meaning "fragrant," a reference to the plant's perfume. It has been cultivated for centuries, for both culinary and medicinal purposes. The sixteenth-century herbalist John Gerard recommended sweet cicely for treating coughs, consumption, digestive upsets, and as a tonic. The roots can be used as a vegetable, either cooked or raw in salads. Its leaves, with their delicate, sweet, anise-like flavor, are traditionally added to *bouquet garni*, soups, stews, or salads and to fruit and cream as a fragrant sweetener. Its seeds, too, can be added to fruit salads or fruit pies.

Other names: Garden myrrh, sweet bracken, sweet chervil

Plant family: Apiaceae

Height: 3–6ft (1–2m)

Habit: Hardy perennial with fern-like leaves and clusters of tiny, white flowers

Habitat: Moist, humus-rich soil in sun or shade

Uses: Culinary, medicinal, decorative

Myrtle

Myrtus communis

Native to the Mediterranean and South-West Europe, this fragrant, flowering shrub can be found growing wild in scrubland but is more usually cultivated. In Ancient Greece, myrtle was considered sacred to Aphrodite, the goddess of love, and traditionally planted near her temples. It is, therefore, used in wedding bouquets in the Middle East. Medicinally, myrtle leaf tea was a soothing expectorant and research has shown that it possesses antibiotic properties. Myrtle berries were eaten in ancient times as a breath-sweetener. Its leaves, flower buds, and berries add flavor to hams, sauces, and meat dishes, particularly in the islands of Corsica and Sardinia.

Plant family: Myrtaceae
Height: 10ft (3m)
Habit: Half-hardy, evergreen, perennial shrub with glossy, dark green, oval leaves and white flowers with golden stamens
Habitat: Well-drained, neutral to alkaline soil in sun
Uses: Culinary, medicinal, decorative

Watercress

Nasturtium officinale
(Rorippa nasturtium-aquaticum)

Native to Europe and Asia, watercress grows in the wild in shallow water in streams, rivers, and ditches and is also widely cultivated. The generic name is derived from the Latin *nasus tortus*, meaning "twisted nose," a reference to the plant's pungent smell. Since ancient times its pleasantly sharp, peppery leaves have been eaten not only for their flavor but for their health-giving properties. The Greek general Xenophon prescribed it to his soldiers as a tonic, while the Ancient Greek physician Hippocrates recommended it as an expectorant and stimulant. Indeed, watercress is rich in vitamins A and C, iron, and other minerals. Today, it is primarily used as a culinary herb, fresh or cooked in salads, soups, and stir-fries and as a garnish, particularly for meat and poultry dishes.

Plant family: Brassicaceae
Height: 4–26in (10–65cm)
Habit: Aquatic, hardy, evergreen perennial with glossy, dark-green, pinnate leaves divided into three to five pairs of ovate leaflets and tiny, four-petaled, white flowers
Habitat: Shallow, flowing, slightly alkaline water in sun
Uses: Culinary, medicinal

Catnip

Nepeta cataria

Native to Europe and East and West Asia, catnip grows in the wild near streams and on roadsides. Its common names "catnip" and "catmint" refer to the plant's well-known effect on felines, who nibble the leaves and roll upon the plant with obvious pleasure. It is thought that the main component of the plant's volatile oil, nepetalactone, resembles a feline sexual pheromone. Despite its enlivening effect on cats, catnip was employed in traditional herbal medicine as a sedative, drunk in infusion form to calm nerves and to treat insomnia, stomach upsets, and colds and influenza. Its leaves can be used to make a mint-flavored tea and added to salads, sauces, and stews. Commercially, the herb's best-known use is in catnip toys for felines.

Other name: Catmint
Plant family: Lamiaceae
Height: 1–5ft (30cm–1.5m)
Habit: Hardy perennial with gray-green, ovate, toothed leaves and small, whitish or pinkish flowers
Habitat: Moist, well-drained soil in sun
Uses: Culinary, medicinal

Basil

Ocimum basilicum

Thought to be native to India and the Middle East, basil is now cultivated around the world, with many varieties available. It was said to have grown round Christ's tomb after the Resurrection and was seen as a symbol of love. It also had a darker side, thought to breed scorpions and associated by the Ancient Greeks and Romans with poverty and misfortune. In culinary terms, basil is particularly linked with Mediterranean cuisine, where it adds its aroma to dishes such as tomato salads, pasta sauces, and soups. Most famously, it is the key ingredient in pesto, a blend of basil, garlic, pine nuts, Parmesan cheese, and olive oil originating from the Italian port of Genoa, hence the name "Genovese." Historic medicinal applications range from a digestive aid to a cough mixture.

Other names: Sweet basil, Genovese
Plant family: Lamiaceae
Height: Up to 20in (50cm)
Habit: A bushy annual with oval, bright green leaves and spires of tiny, white flowers
Habitat: Prefers full sun with fairly rich, freedraining soil
Uses: Culinary, medicinal

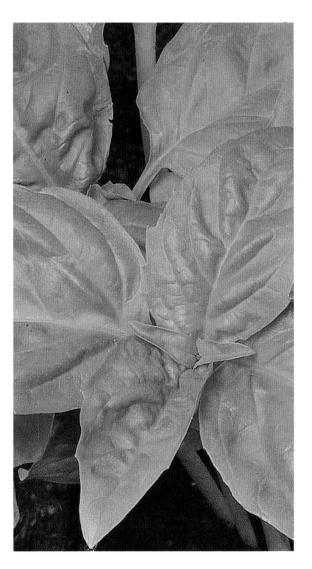

Evening Primrose

Oenothera biennis

Native to North America, the evening primrose grows wild on steep banks, dunes, wasteground, and in fields and is also cultivated. The common name refers to its habit of opening its fragrant, yellow flowers in the early evening. The Native Americans have long valued the plant for its medicinal properties, using it in poultices to treat skin problems and bruises. Today, it is a widely used herb supplement, taken particularly to treat pre-menstrual tension and applied externally to treat eczema. It is also taken to prevent hangovers, rheumatoid arthritis, and ease depression. Research has shown the plant to be high in an oil containing the essential fatty gamma-linolenic acid and there is much pharmaceutical interest in its medical potential.

Other names: Fever plant, night willowherb, tree primrose
Plant family: Onagraceae
Height: 3–5ft (1–1.5m)
Habit: Hardy biennial with long, green, oval or lanceolate leaves and large, bowl-shaped, yellow flowers
Habitat: Well-drained to dry soil in sun
Uses: Medicinal

Sweet Marjoram

Origanum majorana

Native to Southern Europe, North Africa, and Turkey, sweet marjoram grows in the wild in sunny, sheltered spots but is also cultivated for its aromatic leaves. Its popular name of "knotted marjoram" is thought to be a reference to its small, round flower buds, resembling knots on stems. Medicinally, it is a relaxing, warming herb, taken internally for bronchial complaints, headaches, and insomnia. It is as a culinary herb, however, that it is primarily known. Its leaves and flowers, with their delicate scent and sweet, aromatic flavoring, are used fresh and dried in sausages, herb scones, salads, omelets, and sauces and in *bouquet garni*. Dried sweet marjoram is also popular for potpourri.

Other names: Knot marjoram, knotted marjoram
Plant family: Lamiaceae
Height: 2ft (60cm)
Habit: Half-hardy perennial with downy, gray-green, ovate leaves and clusters of small, white to pink flowers
Habitat: Well-drained, average to rich soil in sun
Uses: Culinary, medicinal

Oregano

Origanum vulgare

Native to Europe, oregano favors dry, chalky soil, growing on hillsides in dry pastures and along hedgebanks. The generic name is from the Greek *oros*, meaning "mountain," and *ganos*, meaning "joy." Medicinally, the Ancient Greeks used it as an antidote to poison, as a disinfectant, and a preservative. Today, this aromatic herb, with its pungent flavor, is primarily used in the kitchen. It is particularly associated with Mediterranean cookery, adding flavor in its dried form to dishes such as Italian tomato sauces for pizzas, or hearty Greek stews. Its oil is used commercially in toiletries and perfumes.

Other name: Wild marjoram
Plant family: Lamiaceae
Height: 12–36in (30–90cm)
Habit: Hardy perennial with ovate, green leaves on purplish stems and clusters of pinkish-purple flowers
Habitat: Well-drained to dry, neutral to alkaline soil in sun
Uses: Culinary, medicinal, cosmetic

Opium Poppy

Papaver somniferum

Native to the Mediterranean and Western Asia, but now naturalized in many countries, the opium poppy is also cultivated. Its specific name *somniferum* is derived from the Latin for "sleep-bringing," a reference to its notable narcotic qualities. It has been used as a sedative for many centuries, known to the Ancient Egyptians, Sumerians, and Ancient Greeks. It is the plant from which both opium and morphine are derived and, as such, its cultivation is legally restricted in many countries. Poppy seeds, however, contain no drug and are used in breads and pastries or to thicken dishes such as curries. Its coldpressed oil is used for salad dressings.

Other name: White poppy
Plant family: Papaveraceae
Height: 1–5ft (30cm–1.5m)
Habit: Hardy annual with gray-green, deeply toothed leaves and large, white to pink, to purplish flowers
Habitat: Well-drained soil in sun
Uses: Culinary, medicinal

Rose-scented Geranium

Pelargonium capitatum

Native to South Africa, this low, spreading perennial is now widely grown as a popular garden plant. It is actually a pelargonium, not to be confused with the geranium, despite its misleading common name and similar appearance. Scented-leafed pelargoniums were introduced to Europe in the seventeenth century and have been cultivated since, valued for their fragrant leaves and pretty flowers. In South Africa, the plant was traditionally used medicinally, to treat kidney and digestive disorders. Its perfumed, rose-scented oil is found in geranium oil, used in aromatherapy, perfumery, and cosmetic products.

Other name: Wild rose geranium
Plant family: Geraniaceae
Height: 12–36in (30–90cm)
Habit: Tender perennial with velvety, crinkly, three to five lobed leaves and clusters of pink to pale purple flowers
Habitat: Well-drained, neutral to alkaline soil
Uses: Medicinal, cosmetic, decorative

Parsley

Petroselinum crispum

Today, this most familiar of herbs is taken for granted, perhaps because of its ubiquitous use as a garnish. In fact, parsley has long been a valued medicinal herb, credited by the herbalist Culpeper with treating many diseases, including liver and kidney complaints. There are many beliefs and superstitions associated with it; the Ancient Greeks decorated tombs with parsley and the Ancient Romans wore parsley wreaths at banquets to prevent intoxication. Its long germination time (70 to 90 days) led to the old saying that parsley seed goes six times to the Devil and back before germinating. With its distinctive, yet subtle, fresh flavor, parsley is a widely used culinary herb.

Other name: Curly parsley
Plant family: Apiaceae
Height: 12–16in (30–40cm)
Habit: A hardy biennial with dense heads of small, bright green, curly toothed leaves and flat-topped clusters of creamy white flowers
Habitat: Prefers full sun or light shade and fertile, well-drained soil
Uses: Culinary, medicinal

Solomon's Seal

Polygonatum odoratum

Native to Europe and Asia, Solomon's seal grows in woods and shrublands. There are various theories as to the origins of its striking name. One theory is that Solomon set his seal upon its roots (which resemble broken Hebrew characters) in recognition of its medicinal value. Another suggestion is that the name came about because the plant could seal wounds. Solomon's seal certainly has a long history of medicinal use, known in classical times and in China during the first century AD. In Chinese medicine its rhizomes are used to treat dry coughs, heart disease, and tuberculosis. In Ayurvedic medicine it is seen as an aphrodisiac and a treatment for infertility. The sixteenth-century herbalist Gerard recommended using it either in poultice form or as a herb ale, to glue together broken bones. Today, in Europe, it is primarily grown as an ornamental garden plant.

Plant family: Convallariaceae
Height: 34in (85cm)
Habit: Hardy perennial with ovate, pointed, green leaves and white, waxy, green-tipped flowers
Habitat: Well-drained, rich, moist soil in partial shade
Uses: Medicinal, decorative

Cinquefoil

Potentilla erecta

Native to Northern Europe and West Asia, cinquefoil grows in grassland and on heaths and mountain meadows. The generic name *Potentilla* derives from the Latin *potens*, meaning "powerful," a reference to its curative properties. In traditional medicine, cinquefoil is valued as a strong astringent, taken internally to treat diarrhea and inflammation of the colon. Externally, decoctions of cinquefoil are used to treat hemorrhoids, ulcers, cuts, sores, and burns and as a wash for sore eyes. High in tannin and a red coloring agent, its root was also traditionally employed to tan leather and to dye it red.

Other names: Bloodroot, tormentil, shepherd's knot
Plant family: Rosaceae
Height: 8–12in (20–30cm)
Habit: Hardy perennial with three-lobed, toothed, green leaves and four-petaled, yellow flowers
Habitat: Light, acid soil in sun or light shade
Uses: Medicinal, colorant

Cowslip

Primula veris

Native to Northern and Central Europe, the cowslip grows in the wild in fields and roadside verges in chalky and limestone areas. Its generic name *Primula* derives from the Latin *primus*, meaning "first," referring to its early flowering in the spring. Less poetically, its common name "cowslip" is said to derive from Old English *cuslyppe*, meaning "cowpat." Medicinally, cowslip wine and cowslip tea are valued for their calming, sedative qualities and the herb was used to treat spasms, cramps, and paralytic ailments. Its flowers can be eaten fresh in salads, or candied and used as decoration. This plant should not be collected from the wild, however, as nowadays it is a rare plant.

Other names: Herb Peter, key flower, keys of heaven, paigle

Plant family: Primulaceae

Height: 6–8in (15–20cm)

Habit: Hardy perennial with rough-textured, oblong, green leaves and clusters of small, tubular, yellow flowers

Habitat: Dry, neutral to alkaline soil in sun or partial shade

Uses: Culinary, medicinal, decorative

Primrose

Primula vulgaris

Native to Europe and North Asia, the primrose grows wild in woods, hedgerows, and fields and is also cultivated. Traditionally, it was seen as a medicinal plant, recommended by the Roman natural historian Pliny for rheumatism, gout, and paralysis. The seventeenth-century herbalist Nicholas Culpeper advised using it for healing wounds. Its roots were used to treat headaches and, in fact, the plant does contain salicylates, as in aspirin. It was also a traditional expectorant, employed in the treatment of bronchitis. Today, however, it has little medicinal use. In cookery, its flowers and young leaves can be added to salads and its candied blossoms used to decorate desserts and cakes. Its pretty, pale yellow flowers, which appear as a welcome sign of spring, mean that it has long been a popular garden plant.

Plant family: Primulaceae
Height: 6in (15cm)
Habit: Hardy perennial with wrinkled, green, oblong leaves and pale yellow flowers with notched petals
Habitat: Moist, well-drained soil in sun or shade
Uses: Culinary, medicinal, decorative

Lungwort

Pulmonaria officinalis

Native to Europe, lungwort grows in shady, moist grassland, hedgerows, and woods. Both the generic name "*Pulmonaria*" (derived from the Latin *pulmones*, meaning "lungs") and its common name "lungwort" refer to the mottled leaves' supposed resemblance to lungs. According to the *Doctrine of Signatures*, popular in sixteenth and seventeenth-century Europe, this meant the plant should be prescribed for lung complaints. It was traditionally used for these and to treat coughs, bronchitis, and sore throats. Today, it is little used medicinally, but is an ingredient of the alcoholic drink vermouth.

Other names: Jerusalem cowslip, soldiers and sailors
Plant family: Boraginaceae
Height: 12in (30cm)
Habit: Hardy perennial with white-blotched, ovate, hairy, green leaves and bell-shaped flowers, changing from pink to blue
Habitat: Moist soil in sun or shade
Uses: Medicinal, culinary

Rosemary

Rosmarinus officinalis

Native to the Mediterranean region, this aromatic plant grows wild on dry scrub and is also extensively cultivated. A great cosmetic and culinary herb, rosemary has many legendary associations. Perhaps the best-known story connected with it is a Christian one, which tells how the Virgin Mary, during the flight to Egypt, flung her blue robe over a rosemary bush while resting; when she removed her cloak, the previously white flowers had turned blue in her honor. Another Christian legend has Mary spreading the infant Christ's clothes to dry on a rosemary bush, hence giving the plant its fragrance. Carrying a sprig of rosemary has long been seen as providing protection against evil. Rosemary, too, is a symbol of friendship, love, and fidelity. Thought to improve the memory, rosemary was also worn for remembrance, an association referred to by Shakespeare's Ophelia. Its aromatic leaves were used for strewing, burnt to purify the air, and in toilet waters and hair tonics. In the kitchen, rosemary is often cooked with lamb, its pungent fragrance cutting through the meat's rich fattiness. Because of the leaves' spikiness, it is often used in sprig form rather than chopped.

Plant family: Lamiaceae
Height: Up to 6½ft (2m)
Habit: Evergreen, hardy perennial with dark green, needle-shaped leaves and spires of small, blue-purple flowers
Habitat: Well-drained to dry soil in the sun
Uses: Culinary, cosmetic, decorative

Sorrel

Rumex acetosa

Native to Europe, Asia, and North America, sorrel grows widely in grassland and open woods. The common name "sorrel" is said to come from the Old French *surelle*, meaning "sour," a reference to the plant's tart flavor. It has been used since ancient times as both a culinary and a medicinal herb, eaten by the Ancient Eyptians and the Romans to aid digestion and used for blood-cleansing, diuretic, and cooling purposes. Applied externally, it was a treatment for skin disorders, such as sores, ringworm, and scabs. High in oxalic acid, sorrel should not be consumed in excess; however, it is eaten in salads or cooked as a green vegetable, in omelets, or sauces.

Other names: Common sorrel, garden sorrel, meadow sorrel, sour leaves, sour dock
Plant family: Polygonaceae
Height: 20–48in (50–120cm)
Habit: Hardy perennial with broad, oblong, green leaves, arrow-shaped at the base, and spikes of reddish-green flowers
Habitat: Moist soil in sun or partial shade
Uses: Culinary, medicinal

Rue

Ruta graveolens

Native to Southern Europe, rue grows on dry, rocky slopes and limestone scree and has long been cultivated. Its generic name is from the Greek *reuo*, meaning "to set free," thought to refer to the plant's power to release people from disease. Its common name "herb of grace" derives from the tradition of using rue to sprinkle on holy water. Despite having toxic properties if taken in large quantities, there is a long history of this aromatic herb being used medicinally. It was a traditional treatment for strained eyes and for stimulating menstruation and was also long thought of as a magical herb, offering protection against witchcraft. With its aromatic, bitter taste it is a flavoring for alcoholic drinks, such as grappa.

Other names: Herb of grace, herbygrass
Plant family: Rutaceae
Height: 2ft (60cm)
Habit: Hardy, evergreen perennial with deeply divided, fleshy, gray-green leaves and yellow, four-petaled flowers
Habitat: Well-drained, neutral to alkaline soil in sun
Uses: Medicinal, culinary

Sage

Salvia officinalis

Native to the Mediterranean and North Africa, sage is the commonly cultivated, best-known member of a large genus. It is a herb that has long been valued for its healing properties, as its Latin name *Salvia*, from the verb *salvere*, meaning "to save," indicates. An ancient proverb says simply, "Why should a man die who has sage in his garden?" The Romans and Greeks considered it efficacious against snake bites and for use in general tonics, while in medieval times it was a treatment for colds, fevers, epilepsy, and constipation. For centuries, country folk used sage in a variety of ways: for sage wine, sage tea, to flavor cheese, and in sage tobacco. It was also a mouthwash, a hair tonic, and rubbed on teeth to whiten them. Today, sage is thought of primarily as a culinary herb.

Other names: Common sage, garden sage
Plant family: Lamiaceae
Height: Up to 2ft (60cm)
Habit: Hardy perennial with oval, gray-green leaves and small spikes of purple-blue flowers
Habitat: Full sun and well-drained to dry soil
Uses: Culinary, medicinal

Summer Savory

Satureja hortensis

Native to the Mediterranean, summer savory grows wild on mountainsides and moorland, but is cultivated primarily as a potherb. The generic name *Satureja* comes from the Latin *satyrus*, meaning "satyr," a reference to the plant's supposed aphrodisiac properties. Medicinally, summer savory was used to regulate the digestive system, as an expectorant, and a wash for mouth ulcers. Primarily, however, it has always been seen as a culinary herb, with the Romans adding it as an aromatic, peppery flavor to sauces and stuffings. It is traditionally cooked with foods that are hard to digest, such as beans (hence the name "bean herb"), pork, and cucumber. In French cuisine it is one of the herbs used in *herbes de Provence*.

Other name: Bean herb
Plant family: Lamiaceae
Height: 4–14in (10–35cm)
Habit: Hardy annual with linear to oblong, pointed, green leaves and small, white, pink, or lilac flowers
Habitat: Well-drained to dry, neutral to alkaline soil in sun
Uses: Culinary, medicinal

Winter Savory

Satureja montana

Native to Southern Europe, winter savory grows wild on rocky mountain slopes and dry, sunny places. Similar in flavor to thyme, European savories have been used as herbs for over 2000 years. Known by the Ancient Romans and the Greeks, they were primarily seen as culinary herbs rather than medicinal ones, with winter savory and summer savory (*Satureja hortensis*) being the best-known species. Winter savory has a sharper, spicier, more pungent taste than summer savory and is added to stuffings, marinades, and pickles. Its shrubby qualities mean that winter savory can be planted in gardens as a dwarf hedge or edging plant.

Other name: Mountain savory
Plant family: Lamiaceae
Height: 4–16in (10–40cm)
Habit: Semi-evergreen, hardy, perennial subshrub with leathery, linear, dark green leaves and small, white to purple flowers
Habitat: Well-drained to dry, neutral to alkaline soil in sun
Uses: Culinary, decorative

Milk Thistle

Silybum marianum

Native to Europe, the milk thistle grows wild along roadsides or on waste ground. Its specific name *marianum* derives from the legend that the Virgin Mary's milk ran down its leaves, causing their striking white stains. As its name suggests, it was traditionally thought to be good for breastfeeding women, encouraging their milk. Medicinally, the plant was used to treat depression, with the sixteenth-century herbalist John Gerard calling it "the best remedy that grows against all melancholy diseases." Research has shown it to be high in a flavonolignan called "silymarin," which protects the liver against toxins. Its young leaves, trimmed of their spines, can be eaten as a salad or a cooked vegetable, and its roots, too, can be cooked and eaten.

Other names: Blessed thistle, Our Lady's thistle

Plant family: Asteraceae

Height: 4–5ft (1.2–1.5m)

Habit: Hardy annual or biennial with white-veined, deeply lobed, crinkly leaves, with spiny margins, and purple, thistle-like flowers

Habitat: Well-drained, neutral to alkaline soil in sun

Uses: Culinary, medicinal

Goldenrod

Solidago virgaurea

Native to Europe, goldenrod grows in the wild in wasteground and on hillsides, especially where the ground is rich in silica. The generic name *Solidago* derives from the Latin *solidare*, meaning "to join," a reference to the plant's healing powers. During the Middle Ages, when it was brought back from the Crusades to England, it was known as "heathen wound herb." Its leaves and flowers are used particularly to treat kidney stones and also, according to the seventeenth-century herbalist Culpeper, to fasten loose teeth. A bitter, astringent, relaxant herb, it stimulates the liver and kidneys and reduces inflammation. Externally, it was used in compresses to treat wounds and insect bites.

Other name: European goldenrod
Plant family: Asteraceae
Height: 32in (80cm)
Habit: Hardy perennial with lance-shaped, finely toothed, green leaves and yellow flowers
Habitat: Well-drained, sandy to poor soil in sun
Uses: Medicinal

Betony

Stachys officinalis

Native to Europe, betony grows wild in fields and hedgerows and is popular in wildflower meadows. The generic name *Stachys* derives from the Greek word for an "ear of corn," referring to the plant's flowering spikes. The Ancient Egyptians attributed magical properties to this herb and for centuries it was regarded as possessing special properties. It was cultivated in physic and monastery gardens and also grown in churchgrounds and graveyards to offer protection against witchcraft. In traditional medicine, it was used to treat a wide range of ailments and sicknesses, including head colds, sore throats, gout, and nervous conditions. Today, it has little use as a medicinal application, but its dried leaves are an ingredient in herbal tobacco and snuff.

Other names: Bishopswort, wood betony

Plant family: Lamiaceae

Height: 6–24in (15–60cm)

Habit: Hardy perennial with oblong, scallop-edged, green leaves and spikes of magenta flowers

Habitat: Well-drained soil in sun or partial shade

Uses: Medicinal

125

Comfrey

Symphytum officinale

Native to Europe and West Asia, comfrey grows wild in damp, shady places, particularly near streams and rivers. Both the Roman name *conferva*, meaning "join together" (from which comfrey derives) and the generic name, from the Greek *sympho* meaning "to unite," refer to the plant's healing properties, as do its other common names. For centuries it was used to treat wounds and help set broken bones. Research has discovered that comfrey contains allantoin, which actively promotes the growth of new cells. It has also, however, been connected to liver damage and cancer, so its internal consumption is subject to restrictions. Externally, though, it is still used in herbal medicine, particularly for bruises, sprains, and wounds.

Other names: Boneset, bruisewort, knitbone
Plant family: Boraginaceae
Height: Up to 4ft (1.2m)
Habit: Hardy perennial with large, pointed, ovate-lanceolate leaves and white, pink, or purple bell-like flowers
Habitat: Moist to wet soil in sun or partial shade
Uses: Medicinal

Feverfew

Tanacetum parthenium

Native to Europe, feverfew can be found in hedgerows and wasteground and is cultivated as an ornamental garden plant. The plant's common name "feverfew" refers to its historic, medicinal use as a treatment for fevers. The seventeenth-century herbalist Culpeper noted it as being particularly good for female conditions and also as "very effectual for all pains in the head." Clinical studies have shown that the herb can indeed help migraine sufferers, with two or three leaves of the fresh herb consumed directly, although its bitter taste is not particularly palatable.

Other name: Featherfew
Plant family: Asteraceae
Height: Up to 3ft (90cm)
Habit: Hardy perennial with deeply cut, yellow-green leaves and clusters of daisylike flowers
Habitat: Well-drained to dry, stony soil in sun
Uses: Medicinal, decorative

Tansy

Tanacetum vulgare
(Chrysanthemum vulgare)

Native to Europe, tansy grows in the wild on wasteground and in hedgerows and is cultivated as a garden plant. The name "tansy" derives from the Greek *athanasia*, meaning "immortality," possibly because of the custom of packing dead bodies with tansy leaves to help preserve them until burial. With its pungent-smelling leaves, tansy was long used as a strewing herb and an insecticide. Medicinally, it was valued as a tonic and stimulant, used as an enema to expel worms, and for menstrual problems, though it is now considered dangerous as tansy oil is highly toxic. It is also a herb with a long history of culinary use, with its peppery leaves added to flavor custards, cakes, and puddings in medieval times.

Other name: Bachelor's buttons
Plant family: Asteraceae
Height: 2–4ft (60–120cm)
Habit: Hardy perennial with finely divided, feathery green leaves and clusters of yellow, buttonlike flowers
Habitat: Well-drained to dry, stony soil in sun
Uses: Culinary, medicinal, insecticide

Wood Sage

Teucrium scorodonia

Native to Europe, wood sage grows in the wild in a variety of habitats, including woodland, heathland, and dunes. The generic name *Teucrium* is thought to refer either to a mythological archer at Troy named Teucer, or a medical botanist called Dr Teucer. In traditional herbal medicine, it was particularly valued as a tonic, helping to restore the appetite, especially after attacks of rheumatism or gout. It was also used as a diuretic and to restore menstrual flow and dispel clotted blood beneath bruises. Its bitter leaves, with their hoplike smell and flavor, were a traditional additive in brewing ale and it can be eaten in salads when young and tender.

Other names: Mountain sage, sage-leaved germander
Plant family: Lamiaceae
Height: 12–24in (30–60cm)
Habit: Hardy perennial with coarsely toothed, heart-shaped, grayish-green leaves and small, yellowish-green flowers
Habitat: Light, well-drained, neutral to alkaline, dry or stony soil in sun
Uses: Culinary, medicinal

Thyme

Thymus vulgaris

Native to the Mediterranean, common thyme grows in the wild on rocky ground and is widely cultivated. Its aromatic leaves and antiseptic properties meant that it was used in oil form by the Ancient Egyptians for embalming and by the Ancient Greeks and Romans to perfume baths and to purify rooms. During the Middle Ages, it was carried in posies to ward off disease, and modern research has shown thyme oil to be very effective against bacilli. It is a well-known and widely used culinary herb. In French cuisine it is a key ingredient of *bouquet garni* and *herbes de Provence* and it adds flavor to stews, braised dishes, soups and fish, meat, and vegetable dishes.

Other name: Garden thyme
Plant family: Lamiaceae
Height: 6–12in (15–30cm)
Habit: Hardy perennial with small, linear to elliptic, pointed, gray-green leaves and small, purple to white flowers
Habitat: Light, dry, well-drained soil in sun or partial shade
Uses: Culinary, medicinal, cosmetic

Vervain

Verbena officinalis

Native to Europe, West Asia, and North Africa, verbena grows in the wild along roadsides and on wasteground. It is a herb with many legendary and mythic associations, regarded as magical by the ancient druids and used as an altar plant by the Romans. Christian folklore tells of it growing on Calvary, used to staunch Christ's blood at the Crucifixion. Medicinally, it was seen as something of a cure-all, with the seventeenth-century herbalist Culpeper recommending it for ailments, including jaundice, dropsy, gout, coughs, and diseases of the liver. It was also long thought to be an aphrodisiac. Today, vervain is grown mainly for medicinal purposes and is used in both western and Chinese medicine.

Other names: European vervain, simpler's joy, turkey grass
Plant family: Verbenaceae
Height: 32in (80cm)
Habit: Hardy perennial with deeply lobed, green leaves and spikes of small, mauve flowers
Habitat: Well-drained, moist soil in sun
Uses: Medicinal

Heartsease

Viola tricolor

Found as a wildflower in Europe and North America, heartsease grows wild in grassland or on wasteground and is also cultivated. Its specific name *tricolor* refers to its distinctive, three-colored flowers, combining purple, white, and yellow. It is a herb with a long history of romantic connotations, used as a love charm, as a heart cordial, and to cure broken hearts. Medicinal applications for heartsease include treating eczema, soothing rheumatic pains, and, in syrup form, as a cough medicine. It is a mild diuretic and can be used to cleanse the body and stimulate the metabolism. Its pretty flowers can be added to salads, used to garnish dishes, or frozen in ice cubes to decorate drinks.

Other names: Love-lies-bleeding, wild pansy

Plant family: Violaceae

Height: 6–12in (15–30cm)

Habit: Hardy annual, biennial, or short-lived perennial with heartshaped, toothed, green leaves and purple, white, and yellow-colored flowers

Habitat: Well-drained, moist, humus-rich soil in sun or partial shade

Uses: Culinary, medicinal, decorative

Appendix: Table of **usage**

Herbs have been renowned for centuries for their wide range of uses and applications. Traditionally, they have been categorized as being primarily for aromatic, culinary, medicinal, or ornamental use, but this system throws up problems, as so many herbs have multiple uses! The following chart details all the properties of the herbs featured in this book, as well as providing the principal common name for each one.

Table of Usage

Scientific Name	Common Name	Uses
Achillea ageratum	English Mace	Culinary, decorative, medicinal
Achillea millefolium	Yarrow	Culinary, medicinal, cosmetic
Aconitum napellus	Monkshood	Medicinal
Agastache foeniculum	Anise Hyssop	Culinary, decorative, medicinal
Agrimonia eupatoria	Agrimony	Culinary, medicinal
Ajuga reptans	Bugle	Medicinal, decorative
Alchemilla vulgaris	Lady's Mantle	Medicinal
Alliaria petiolata	Jack-by-the-Hedge	Culinary, medicinal
Allium sativum	Garlic	Culinary, medicinal
Allium schoenoprasum	Chives	Culinary, medicinal
Aloe vera (A. barbadensis)	Aloe Vera	Medicinal
Aloysia triphylla	Lemon Verbena	Culinary, medicinal, cosmetic
Althaea officinalis	Marsh Mallow	Culinary, medicinal, cosmetic
Anethum graveolens	Dill	Culinary, medicinal
Angelica archangelica	Angelica	Culinary, cosmetic
Anthriscus cerefolium	Chervil	Culinary, medicinal
Apium graveolens	Wild Celery	Culinary, medicinal
Arctium lappa	Burdock	Culinary, medicinal
Armoracia rusticana (A. lapathifolia, Cochlearia armoracia)	Horseradish	Culinary, medicinal
Arnica montana	Arnica	Medicinal

Scientific Name	Common Name	Uses
Artemisia abrotanum	Southernwood	Culinary, medicinal, decorative, repellent
Artemisia absinthium	Wormwood	Medicinal, culinary
Artemisia dracunculus	Tarragon	Culinary, medicinal
Artemisia vulgaris	Mugwort	Culinary, medicinal
Bellis perennis	Daisy	Culinary, medicinal
Borago officinalis	Borage	Culinary, medicinal
Calamintha grandiflora	Calamint	Medicinal, decorative
Calendula officinalis	Marigold	Culinary, medicinal, cosmetic, colorant
Cardamine pratensis	Lady's Smock	Culinary, medicinal
Carthamus tinctorius	Safflower	Culinary, colorant
Carum carvi	Caraway	Culinary, medicinal
Centaurium erythraea	Centaury	Medicinal
Chamaemelum nobile	Chamomile	Medicinal, culinary, decorative
Cichorium intybus	Chicory	Culinary, medicinal, colorant
Claytonia perfoliata	Winter Purslane	Culinary
Convallaria majalis	Lily-of-the-Valley	Medicinal, decorative
Coriandrum sativum	Coriander	Culinary, medicinal
Cymbopogon citratus	Lemongrass	Culinary, medicinal, repellent
Dianthus caryophyllus	Clove Pink	Culinary, medicinal, decorative
Drosera rotundifolia	Sundew	Medicinal, decorative
Echinacea purpurea	Echinacea	Medicinal

Table of Usage

Scientific Name	Common Name	Uses
Echium vulgare	Viper's Bugloss	Culinary, medicinal
Eschscholzia californica	California Poppy	Medicinal, culinary
Eucalyptus globulus	Eucalyptus	Medicinal, decorative
Eupatorium purpureum	Joe Pye Weed	Medicinal, decorative
Filipendula ulmaria (*Spiraea ulmaria*)	Meadowsweet	Culinary, medicinal, decorative
Foeniculum vulgare	Fennel	Culinary, medicinal, decorative
Fragaria vesca	Wild Strawberry	Culinary, medicinal
Galega officinalis	Goat's Rue	Medicinal
Galium odoratum	Sweet Woodruff	Medicinal, culinary, repellent
Galium verum	Lady's Bedstraw	Culinary, medicinal, colorant
Gardenia augusta	Gardenia	Medicinal, decorative, colorant
Gaultheria procumbens	Wintergreen	Medicinal, culinary
Gentiana lutea	Yellow Gentian	Medicinal, culinary
Hamamelis virginiana	Witch Hazel	Medicinal, decorative
Helichrysum italicum (*H. augustifolium*)	Curry Plant	Culinary, decorative
Hypericum perforatum	St John's Wort	Medicinal, decorative
Hyssopus officinalis	Hyssop	Culinary, medicinal, cosmetic
Inula helenium	Elecampane	Medicinal, decorative
Iris germanica var. *florentina*	Orris	Culinary, medicinal, cosmetic, decorative
Juniperus communis	Juniper	Medicinal, culinary

Scientific Name	Common Name	Uses
Laurus nobilis	Bay	Culinary, medicinal
Lavandula angustifolia	Lavender	Culinary, medicinal, cosmetic, repellent
Lepidium sativum	Cress	Culinary, medicinal
Levisticum officinale	Lovage	Culinary, medicinal
Lonicera periclymenum	Honeysuckle	Medicinal, cosmetic, decorative
Lythrum salicaria	Purple Loosestrife	Medicinal
Melissa officinalis	Lemon Balm	Culinary, medicinal
Mentha pulegium	Pennyroyal	Culinary, medicinal, repellent
Mentha x piperita	Peppermint	Culinary, medicinal
Mentha spicata	Spearmint	Culinary, medicinal, repellent
Monarda didyma	Bergamot	Culinary, medicinal, decorative
Myrrhis odorata	Sweet Cicely	Culinary, medicinal, decorative
Myrtus communis	Myrtle	Culinary, medicinal, decorative
Nasturtium officinale (Rorippa nasturtium-aquaticum)	Watercress	Culinary, medicinal
Nepeta cataria	Catnip	Culinary, medicinal
Ocimum basilicum	Basil	Culinary, medicinal
Oenothera biennis	Evening Primrose	Medicinal
Origanum majorana	Sweet Marjoram	Culinary, medicinal
Origanum vulgare	Oregano	Culinary, medicinal, cosmetic
Papaver somniferum	Opium Poppy	Culinary, medicinal

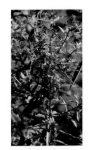

Table of Usage

Scientific Name	Common Name	Uses
Pelargonium capitatum	Rose-scented Geranium	Medicinal, cosmetic, decorative
Petroselinum crispum	Parsley	Culinary, medicinal
Polygonatum odoratum	Solomon's Seal	Medicinal, decorative
Potentilla erecta	Cinquefoil	Medicinal, colorant
Primula veris	Cowslip	Culinary, medicinal, decorative
Primula vulgaris	Primrose	Culinary, medicinal, decorative
Pulmonaria officinalis	Lungwort	Medicinal, culinary
Rosmarinus officinalis	Rosemary	Culinary, cosmetic, decorative
Rumex acetosa	Sorrel	Culinary, medicinal
Ruta graveolens	Rue	Medicinal, culinary
Salvia officinalis	Sage	Culinary, medicinal
Satureja hortensis	Summer Savory	Culinary, medicinal
Satureja montana	Winter Savory	Culinary, decorative
Silybum marianum	Milk Thistle	Culinary, medicinal
Solidago virgaurea	Goldenrod	Medicinal
Stachys officinalis	Betony	Medicinal
Symphytum officinale	Comfrey	Medicinal
Tanacetum parthenium	Feverfew	Medicinal, decorative
Tanacetum vulgare (Chrysanthemum vulgare)	Tansy	Culinary, medicinal, insecticide
Teucrium scorodonia	Wood Sage	Culinary, medicinal
Thymus vulgaris	Thyme	Culinary, medicinal, cosmetic
Verbena officinalis	Vervain	Medicinal
Viola tricolor	Heartsease	Culinary, medicinal, decorative

Index

Index

Bibliography

Bremness, Lesley. *Herbs*. London: Dorling Kindersley, 1994.

Bremness, Lesley. *Pocket Encyclopedia: Herbs*. London: Dorling Kindersley, 1990.

Brown, Deni. *Encyclopedia of Herbs*. London: Dorling Kindersley, 2002.

Buczacki, Stefan. *Best Kitchen Herbs*. London: Hamlyn, 2000.

Davidson, Alan. *The Oxford Companion to Food*. Oxford: Oxford University Press, 2006.

Foley, Caroline, Jill Nice and Marcus Webb. *A New Herb Bible*. Newton Abbott: David and Charles, 2002.

Hemphill, Rosemary. *The Penguin Book of Herbs and Spices*. London: Penguin Books, 1982.

Mabey, David and Rose Mabey. *Jams, Pickles, and Chutneys*. London: Penguin Books, 1983.

McVicar, Jekka. *Jekka's Complete Herb Book*. London: Kyle Cathie, 1997.

McVicar, Jekka. *Jekka's Cottage Garden Herbs*. London: Kyle Cathie, 1995.

Phillips, Roger and Nicky Foy. *Herbs*. London: Pan Books Ltd, 1992.

Robertson, Bruce. *Herb Growing*. London: Chapmans, 1990.

Stobart, Tom. *Herbs, Spices, and Flavorings*. London: Grub Street, 1998.

Tabor, Roger. *All About Herbs*. London: Frances Lincoln, 2002.

Zabar, Abbie. *The Potted Herb*. New York: Stewart, Tabori & Chang, 2003.

Picture credits

The publisher would like to thank the following photographers and picture agencies for their kind permission to reproduce their images in this book:

Harry Chambers: 5, 8b, 9t&b, 10b, 11t&b, 12b, 14t, 14l&r, 15l&r, 16b, 17t, 18l, 19l&r, 19b, 20l, 21b, 24, 25, 34, 35, 36, 37, 38, 39, 40, 42, 43, 45, 46, 47, 48, 50–51, 52, 53, 55, 58, 59, 62, 64, 72, 81, 82, 83, 84, 87, 88–9, 91, 93, 94, 95, 96, 99, 100, 102, 103, 104, 105, 106–7, 109, 110, 114, 116–17, 118, 119, 120, 121, 122, 123, 126, 127, 128, 129, 130–31, 132, 133

Oxford Scientific Films:
Bill Boch 86; Rex Butcher 57, 134–5; Brian Carter 69; David Cavagnaro 60, 61; Gulin Darrell 18t; Richard Day 70; Professor Jack Dermid 18r, 73; Rosalie Frost 80; Christopher Gallagher 16t; Bob Gibbons 63; John Glover 27; Mark Hamblin 10t, 113; Sunniva Harte 31, 115; Donald Higgs 124; IFA-Bilderteam GMBH 49, 65; Ward Kennan 68; Geoff Kidd/OSF 8t; Tom Leach 79; Gordon Maclean 30, 74, 85, 143; P L Martin 71; Colin Milkins 54; Steven Needham Mark 66; John Neubauer 2, 98; Richard Packwood 235; Photolibrary Group 101; Howard Rice 92; Pomerantz Rich 17b; J S Sira 22–3, 111; Mike Slater 67, 76; TH FOTO 44; TH Poto Werbung 90; Juliette Wade 125; Eberhart Wally 20r, 97, 108; Rachel Weill 41; W. Wisniewski 26

Corbis 13, 29, 56, 75, 77, 78, 112

Cover image: Sprigs of flowers © Lisa Hubbard/Getty images

The publisher would also like to thank all the staff at the National Herb Center at Warmington, UK, for all their assistance and advice during the making of this book.